Streamside Guide

COMPLETELY REVISED
ALL-COLOR EDITION

Dave Hughes

Frank
Amato
PORTLAND

Western Streamside Guide

**COMPLETELY REVISED
ALL-COLOR EDITION**

DAVE HUGHES

Frank Amato

PORTLAND

DEDICATION

For Frank Amato.
Like so many Western fishing writers,
I owe my start,
and most of the good things
that have happened since, to Frank.

ABOUT THE AUTHOR

 Dave Hughes is an amateur aquatic entomologist. He has spent more than thirty years fly fishing Western waters, studying and photographing the insects trout eat and the fly patterns that match them. His articles and essays have appeared in *Flyfishing, Salmon Trout Steelheader, Fly Fisherman, Gray's Sporting Journal* and *Fly Rod & Reel* magazines.

Dave lives in Portland, Oregon, with his wife, Masako Tani and daughter, Kosumo.

OTHER FRANK AMATO PUBLICATIONS TITLES BY DAVE HUGHES:

Complete Book of Western Hatches
(co-authored with Rick Hafele)
An Angler's Astoria
American Fly Tying Manual
Deschutes
The Yellowstone River and its Angling
Dry Fly Fishing
Nymph Fishing

© 1998 by Dave Hughes
Frank Amato Publications, Inc.
P.O. Box 82112, Portland, Oregon 97282
503•653•8108
Fly photography by Jim Schollmeyer
All other photos by author except where otherwise noted.
Book and Cover Design: Kathy Johnson
Printed in Hong Kong, China
Softbound ISBN: 1-57188-112-3
Hardbound ISBN: 1-57188-124-7
1 3 5 7 9 10 8 6 4 2

TABLE OF CONTENTS

CHAPTER 1

OBSERVATION AND IMITATION

THE VARIED GEOGRAPHY OF THE WEST HAS LED TO the evolution of a wonderful and confusing array of aquatic and terrestrial insect species. Most of these suffer moments of vulnerability to trout at one time or another. If a species becomes suddenly abundant and easily available, trout might even become selective to it. If you're fishing where and when it happens, that species is the most important insect in the world *at that instant.*

This does not necessarily mean the insect is an important hatch. For many species of insects, those moments of importance are rare, very brief, or isolated to a few regional streams or stillwaters. Some species hatch in numbers that, for reasons known only to nature, make them important in one spike season nested among an infinity of seasons when you'd waste space in your fly boxes carrying their imitations.

Separating the important hatches from those that are not worth bothering to match, is the first step in constructing a fly box that has value over the extended geographical region that is the West, during the long period of the year that is the Western trout season. If you carry flies to match the most important hatches, you'll rarely encounter a minor hatch that you cannot match with a fly that you already have on you.

Four factors define the most important Western hatches: *widespread distribution*, *abundance*, *concentrated numbers*, and *availability to trout*. If an insect hatches nearly everywhere in the West, then you're likely to run into it some time or another, either on your home waters or in your travels. If the insect hatches in good numbers it is far more likely to be important to trout, and therefore to you, than one represented in the diet by a scattering of individual specimens. Scattered hatches will be taken by trout, but not often selectively. If the insect emerges, falls to the water from streamside foliage, or is blown onto the water from bankside grasses in good numbers over a short time period, then trout will see enough of them to become selective to them.

This does not mean that the insects must appear on the water in hundreds or thousands all at the same time. It does mean that more of a particular insect must be around than any other. If trout see a wide variety of insect types at any given time they'll feed opportunistically. You will not need a specific imitation of any one of them. If trout see a concentration of a single insect type they'll develop a search image for it, and take only a fly pattern that fits the image. You will need to imitate it.

It might seem foolish to mention that the insect must be available to trout before it becomes important to match it. But I must confess I've wasted time tying and fishing imitations that were never needed because trout did not get much chance to feed selectively on the naturals. Think for a moment about mosquitoes. It's the rare angler who has not noticed that these can be abundant around trout waters. Fly pattern books offer plenty of imitations for them. These flies catch trout, but not necessarily because trout feed selectively on the naturals the flies imitate. Mosquito larvae require water that is standing and just inches deep. That describes swamps and backwaters and shallow catchbasins, not trout water. You'll often find mosquitoes abundant enough to drive you crazy while you're fishing, but trout rarely find them abundant and available where they're feeding.

This book is about those relatively few insects and other food forms that have widespread geographical distribution throughout the Western states and provinces, that are abundant in numbers, concentrated in time, and that hatch or fall to the water in a way that makes them available often enough to prompt trout to feed selectively. These are the food forms for which you should carry matching patterns.

■ Observation

To determine what you need to imitate when you're out fishing, you must make some broad observations. The first thing to look for is the presence of visibly feeding trout. If trout are not feeding high enough in the water column that you can see it happening, they probably aren't feeding selectively. Most of the time, when trout hold along the bottom in moving water or deep in lakes and ponds, they feed opportunistically and will accept whatever fly tumbles or swims to them so long as it has some resemblance to the general run of naturals they've been taking.

Rises are the surest sign of actively feeding trout. They are not always easy to see. Some of the most selective trout sip so quietly that the riseform barely dimples the surface film. If the water is at all wrinkled, as in a slight riffle or choppy run, such rises are almost impossible to notice if you do not watch very carefully. You will do more to improve your trout fishing success by learning to slow down and watch the water patiently for working fish than you will by honing any other single skill.

If trout do not feed visibly at the surface itself, watch for signs that they're holding or cruising just beneath the surface or slightly deeper, in the mid-depths. At times you can even see trout feeding along the bottom, their silver sides sending winks to your eye as they turn to take insects adrift along the bottom. Patient observation is the key to noticing what trout are doing at any level, which then becomes the key to figuring out how to catch them.

If you spot feeding trout at any level, the next thing to look for is the food-form causing the activity. If trout feed on the bottom, dip down with a kick screen net, or roll up your sleeves and hoist some rocks off the bottom. If they feed in the mid-depths, suspend a net of some sort in the current to capture what they are taking. If trout feed on emergers stuck in the surface film, the cause will most often be mayflies or midges in the smallest sizes, because those are the most common insects that get trapped in the surface film.

When trout feed on the surface itself, the cause is almost always the adult stage of some insect that has emerged from beneath the water, or a terrestrial insect that has fallen to it. An aquarium net, your cupped hand, or your hat are all you need to capture whatever they're taking.

Take time to be sure they are taking the insect that is most visible on the water. I've seen times when trout seemed to be feeding on fairly large and obvious insects, say size 12 March brown mayflies or size 16 pale morning duns. A closer look, which can be done by peering right into a trout's feeding lane with binoculars or wading out, scattering the trout, and then snooping right into their feeding lanes, will reveal some smaller insect, most often a size 18 or 20 little olive, floating among the larger ones. Trout, when given a choice, seem to prefer these smaller bites. If you never notice them, you'll never be able to match them.

The goal of observation is to determine precisely which stage of which insect to imitate.

■ Recognition

It's not necessary to identify the species of an insect in order to imitate it. All you need to do is observe its size, form, and color, then pick a fly pattern that resembles it in the same three key aspects. However, your success and also your pleasure will take a sudden jump up if you learn to recognize the insect hatches at some basic level. You do not need to become an entomologist, nor do you need to invest in a fancy microscope and a bunch of thick biological books to accomplish this.

What you do need is a list of the salient features of each of the most important hatches, and a couple of simple tools that help you observe them fairly closely. The first tool I'd advise you to get is the aquarium net I've already mentioned. A good one will cost you a couple of bucks. With it you'll be able to lift specimens from the current that might otherwise slip between your fingers. You can sweep it through weeds to see what's living in them. If you lift rocks from the bottom while holding the net just downstream, what flits away to escape, dashes right into the meshes. You can lift it out and observe it. The simple aquarium net is the single best investment you can make to begin getting a closer look at the insects you're about to imitate.

The second purchase I'd advise will also open your eyes to the aquatic world in a profound way. It's a high-quality, hand-held loupe in 10X. They're available at The Nature Company stores, and no doubt many other places, for around twenty-five to thirty dollars. I now carry one that is 10X at one end, 15X at the other. It dangles around my neck on a cord whenever I'm fishing. It allows a close look at the parts of an insect that become its key identifying features: legs, antennae, gills, and other peripheral parts. A loupe lets you separate out the parts of an insect you're about to imitate, and look at each part closely, perhaps for the first time. That is the most important thing the loupe brings to you: this ability to notice the precise size, shape, and color of the insect and its individual parts.

A loupe will make a far more careful observer of you. It will, as an accidental adjunct, open your eyes to the wonder of tiny streamside flowers, the symmetry of grass blades and tree seeds and all other things in nature that we believe are at the edges of our fishing but are truly central to it.

Once you've acquired an aquarium net and loupe, then you can use the descriptions in this book to recognize the insects you collect to a useful level. Recognition allows you to move on to the selection of an appropriate imitation.

■ Imitation

The stage of the insect you've collected dictates the type of fly pattern you'll choose to imitate it. If the natural is a nymph or larva, you'll imitate it with a nymph. If it's a pupa or drowned adult, your best bet will be a soft-hackle or wet fly. If it's an emerger, you'll want to fish with a dressing that floats flush in the surface film. If the insect is an adult, most often you'll want to imitate it with a dry fly, though there are certain insects you can imitate better, even in their winged adult stages, with fly patterns that sink.

Once you've chosen a fly type—nymph, wet, emerger, or dry—then the water type in which you'll fish it predicates the fly style you should try. If the fly is a dry, you'll want one that is hackled for flotation in fast water, one that has no hackle to interfere with its silhouette if you'll be fishing it on smooth water. If it's a nymph, you'll want one that is heavily weighted for deep and fast water, and one that is lightly weighted, or not weighted at all, if the water is shallow and slow. If the water is fast, a suggestive wet fly such as a soft-hackle might be best. If it is slow and trout will get a good look at your imitation, your wet fly might fish better if it looks more precisely like the insect you're imitating.

The goal of imitation is to select a fly pattern that imitates the insect *in the circumstance where you'll fish it*. Don't use the most exact imitation, a fragile no-hackle dry fly for example, in water that is too rough for it to float. Don't use a heavily hackled dressing on water so smooth that you need to show an unobstructed silhouette, but where flotation is not necessary.

Always select your imitation based on the way you want it to fish in the water where you intend to fish it.

▌ Presentation

The final goal, which brings observation, recognition, and imitation together, is *proper presentation*. Your chosen method should be based in large part on the behavior of the natural. That is one reason recognition of an insect is so helpful. You can always choose a fly pattern based on the size, form, and color of any natural you observe. But if you can recognize it, even on a basic level, then you will suddenly know a lot about its behavior: how it moves on or in the water. That will tell you how to present its imitation.

Your presentation is chosen according to the natural you're trying to imitate. Your rigging is based on the way you want to fish that imitation. If you're fishing a dry fly, you'll want to rig with a leader the length of the rod or a bit longer on fast water, a 12- to 14-foot leader with a long and fine tippet on water that is smooth or even still. If you're fishing the mid-depths with wet flies or nymphs, the same rigging will work well enough. But if you're fishing the depths, tumbling an imitation along the bottom or probing around weed

beds in lakes and ponds, you will need to rig with a strike indicator and split shot, or choose some sort of sinking-line system to get your fly down deep enough in a stillwater. Again, the way you rig is dictated by the way you want to fish your fly.

Presentation itself is based on the way the natural appears before the trout. It is also based on the water type in which you're fishing, and the limits of the situation in which you find yourself. For example, you might desire to fish a dry fly upstream to rising trout, but find that the shape of the water, perhaps its depth or the speed and force of the current, will not allow you to move into position for an upstream cast. So you take the best position you can, according not only to what you're using, but also to what the water will allow you to do. Then you base your presentation on where you are and what kind of cast you can make.

■ Summation

When you encounter any hatch, these are the four basic things to do, in the order that you want to do them. The first is *observation*, telling you what the trout are doing, and if they're feeding, which stage of what critter they are taking. The second is *recognition*, determining what you can discover about the taxonomy and behavior of the insect with which you are dealing. The third is *imitation*, which is the key problem of selecting a fly pattern to fish properly in the situation. The final element is *presentation*, which brings together all of the other factors and allows you to show your fly to the trout in the way the naturals arrive.

The purpose of this *Western Streamside Guide* is not to tell you precisely where and when you will encounter each hatch. It is, rather, to prepare you to fish over the most common and therefore most important hatches in the West, wherever and whenever you find them. These are the hatches you will almost surely encounter in the course of a trout fishing season. If you are prepared, you will seldom get caught short of a pattern that will take trout, anywhere throughout the West, any time during the year.

The hatches covered in this book, though in no seeming order at a casual glance, are ordered roughly as you might encounter them throughout the angling season. They are never lined up like dominoes. Hatch times vary with latitude, altitude, water temperature, and the weather. Some hatches come off all year long, or scattered at various times through the year. Often two species in a single group, indistinguishable to you and to the trout and to everyone else except taxonomists, might emerge at opposite ends of the season, though they'll be fished with precisely the same dressings. Take these hatches when and where you find them. Always be ready to match them and you'll rarely fail to fool a few trout when they suddenly get selective.

CHAPTER 2

MIDGES

Order: Diptera
Family: Chironomidae

IF YOU FISH MUCH IN WINTER, MIDGES ARE THE FIRST
hatch you're likely to encounter. They emerge all year,
but tend to have their moments of most importance
when other aquatic insect hatches have not yet started,
or have ended.

I use the term *midge* in the biological sense, as a
common name for two-winged insects in the family
Chironomidae. In the angling sense, the term midge is
often used to mean any small insect and, by extension,
any small fly. Though most midges are indeed small,
some Chironomid species are so large you tie their imitations on size 10 hooks, long shank.

Midges are related to mosquitoes and are often
mistaken for them, though they lack the probing proboscis. Many dressings actually tied to match midge
pupae and adults have been mistakenly called
Mosquitoes. Midges are common in trout water, both
moving and still. Mosquitoes prefer standing water just
inches deep. They are rarely important to the angler
except as something to swat at and curse.

Midges have a complete life cycle, passing through
larval, pupal, and adult stages before mating in
swarms, sometimes high in the air, and laying their
eggs on the water. It's probable that more midges are
eaten in the larval stage than any other, but I don't
assign much importance to larvae as a stage worth imitating. In lakes and ponds they live in bottom silt and
on the stems and leaves of rooted vegetation. In
streams they feed on the thin film of diatoms and algae
on bottom stones. Trout take midge larvae in great
numbers, but in my experience not selectively. If some
other food form happens by, trout usually accept it as
well. The other creature is almost always easier to
imitate than a midge larva, so I don't list ties for them.

Pupation takes place in a cocoon on the bottom or
in vegetation. When ready to emerge, pupae float
toward the surface, propelling themselves with a feeble
swimming action. They are extremely vulnerable to
trout during this period, and often pass through the
mid-depths of stillwaters in great enough numbers that

trout become selective to them down where it's almost impossible to know it is happening.

The surface film is a barrier to the passage of tiny insects, especially on calm days. If the pupae are large, say size 14 and up, they have enough mass to break right through. If the tension is broken by a breeze on a lake or by a riffle in a stream, midge pupae pass through with no trouble. If the tension becomes a barrier, small midge pupae tend to hang below it in great numbers, all attempting to break through. Trout ease along slowly and pluck them from the rafters like berries. This creates the most common selective situation with midges.

The next stage of importance is the emerger, sometimes called the *stillborn* midge. The pupa breaks the film. The adult gets halfway out of the pupal exoskeleton. Progress gets halted there for some anatomical anomoly or condition of wind and weather. If enough midges get stuck in their shucks, trout become selective to these stillborns and you'll need to imitate them to catch many trout.

The fully-formed adult does not remain on the water for long. Trout will take traditionally hackled midge dry flies during a hatch, and these dressings are well worth carrying, but I suspect they are mistaken as often for emergers as they are for winged adults. However, such speculations mean more to anglers than they do to trout. If a pattern style works during a hatch, it is valuable to have in the fly box in the range of colors in which the naturals are most common.

Midges often emerge in such great numbers that they gather in clusters and swirl along on top of the water. This usually happens on the smooth surface of a spring creek or meadow stream, any time of day in cold weather or at dusk when the weather is normal. Trout take these clustered midges by the mouthful. Your imitation can be much larger than one imitating a single specimen of the species that is active at the instant. This allows you to fish a fly that is easier to see, and more likely to hold a large trout once you hook it.

Look for midges to be most important on ponds, lakes, and in stretches of streams where the water is relatively smooth on top. Spring creeks and tailwaters with stabilized flows, silt bottoms, and rooted vegetation have heavier populations of midges than do faster freestone streams. But the backwaters and eddies of any stream or river will produce important hatches of midges.

Midges are important in most waters open to winter angling. I've seen excellent tailwater hatches, with trout feeding selectively, when the water temperature was a frigid 38 degrees and the air temperature not much higher. During such conditions it is likely that midges are the only insect around. If conditions improve and other insects hatch, trout might or might not turn to them, too. Midges often get masked by larger mayflies or caddis that the trout are actually ignoring. You'll notice the larger insects, match them, not do well, and overlook an abundance of size 22 to 26 midges on which the trout are truly feeding. Such situations are frustrating until you suspend an aquarium net in the water and lift it out to find its meshes speckled with tiny dots. Use your loupe to look at them closely. Those dots might contain the solution to your frustration. Refine your tackle to suit tiny flies, fish them on a short line, and you'll soon be stinging trout.

Midges can be important through the entire season, as well as in winter. They are especially so in midsummer on ponds, or on lakes too small or too shallow to stratify, when other hatches taper off due to the heat. Midges keep hatching, usually mid-morning and again in the evening. If you see trout rising, observe no other insects around, and cannot figure out what is going on, suspect midges. Spend some time with your nose close to the water, especially along a windward shore. If you see rafts of abandoned midge shucks blown there, you'll know the trout are feeding on rising midge pupae or on those adrift just beneath the film.

In warm southern latitudes, roughly across southern California, Arizona, and New Mexico, midge species might have four to five generations per season. Each generation has a short time to grow, so individuals at emergence are small. As you go north, the number of generations per year dwindles and the time each cycle spends growing in the larval stage is increased. In the Kamloops region of Canada, where one or two generations are the rule, midge pupal imitations are often tied on 3X long hooks in size 8 and 10.

■ Recognition

Midge pupae have small swimmer paddles at the end of the abdomen, often as whitish fringes or tufts. The abdomen is long and slender, usually with clearly defined segmentation. The thorax is bunched and the head is held in front of it, or ventrally, giving a hunchback appearance to the insect. The wing pads are short and extend along the sides. The head is capped with a wig of gill tufts. They vary from a tiny size 26 up to size 8.

The adult midge has a long abdomen tapered almost to a point. The single pair of wings is held flat over the back, the tips short of the end of the abdomen. The hindwings have evolved into short knobbed stalks called *halteres*. The legs of the adult are long and very fragile. Male adults have feathery antennae that are used to pick up the wing beat frequency of females of the same species. Females lack these antennae, look like mosquitoes, but do not have the proboscis.

■ Key Characteristics

Midge pupae: Swimmer paddles.
Humpbacked thorax.
Short wing pads.
Gill tufts on head.
Size: 8 to 26.
Common colors: Black, brown, olive, and tan.

MIDGE PUPA

MIDGE ADULT

Midge adults: Slender abdomen.
Short wings.
Long, fragile legs.
Knobbed stalks, called *halteres*, under wings.
Plume-like antennae of males.
Size: 10 to 26.
Common colors: Black, brown, olive, and tan.

■ Imitation

For pupae in size 16 and smaller, it is necessary to imitate only the elongated abdomen and the bunched thorax and wing pads. A bit of dubbing on the hook, twisted tightly over the back two-thirds and picked out slightly at the front third, will do an excellent job. Add tinsel or wire ribbing for the segmentation if you desire. This is the Traditional Midge Pupa dressing.

For pupal patterns size 14 and up, it is beneficial to imitate the segmentation of the abdomen plus the gill tufts at the head. The TDC, short for Thompson's Delectible Chironomid and originated by Washington biologist Dick Thompson, is one of the best midge pupa patterns, and also an excellent style upon which to base a series of color variations. If you plan to fish any pattern in the mid-depths to imitate rising pupae, weight the dressing with lead wire wrapped around the hook shank. If you intend to suspend the fly just beneath the film, tie it without weight.

Emergers or stillborns are best imitated with patterns that float flush in the surface film. My favorite dressing style is the Sangre de Cristo Emerger, first brought to my attention by members of the Sangre de Cristo Flyfishers in Santa Fe, New Mexico while we were fishing a beaver pond reach of the Cimmaron River. The Griffith's Gnat, with its peacock herl body and palmer of grizzly hackle, is one I would never want to be caught without. When I'm fishing relatively still water and encounter trout feeding on invisibles, it's the first fly I try, sometimes before collecting to see what is happening. It solves a lot of selective situations, surprisingly often when it even fails to look anything like the natural that is hatching.

The Traditional Midge Adult is an easy fly to tie, which is a blessing when you're tying on size 22 to 26 hooks. In the smallest sizes your working thread becomes the body. A tail and a few turns of hackle are all that you need to create a killing pattern.

I use my own Palmered Midge style, in a narrow range of colors, to imitate clustered midges. It often works well even when trout are not obviously feeding on bunched midges. It is easy to see on the water. If trout are willing to sip it, that makes fishing over a midge hatch a lot easier.

I've had excellent luck fishing Sylvester Nemes's Syl's Midge soft-hackle during any stage of the midge hatch on moving water. It's a simple tie, and is fished sunk, on the swing. You can feel the take, which means you no longer need to follow the drift of a tiny dry fly on the surface. If light is low, say at dusk or during rain or even snow under a leaden sky, fishing Syl's Midge is an excellent way to catch some trout rather than giving up and wading out.

Traditional Midge Pupa

Hook: 2X heavy or standard dry fly, size 12 to 24.
Weight: 10 to 15 turns lead wire, optional.
Thread: 6/0 or 8/0 nylon to match body color.

TRADITIONAL MIDGE PUPA

Ribbing: Gold or silver wire or fine oval tinsel.
Abdomen: Black, brown, olive, or tan fur.
Thorax: Same as abdomen, thicker and picked out.

TDC (Dick Thompson)
Hook: 1X long, size 8 to 22.
Weight: 10 to 15 turns lead wire, optional.
Thread: Black 6/0 or 8/0 nylon.
Rib: Fine silver tinsel or wire.
Body: Black fur or wool yarn.
Thorax: Same as body, tied thicker.
Collar: White or cream ostrich herl.

TDC

Note: This is the original, and the most useful in the style. You can base color variations on the TDC by using brown, tan, or olive fur or yarn. It's possible you'll collect midge pupae in other colors as well, in which case you will want to match them if trout are feeding selectively on them.

Sangre de Cristo Midge
Hook: Standard dry fly, size 16 to 24.
Thread: 8/0 nylon to match body color.

SANGRE DE CRISTO MIDGE

Wing post: White closed-cell foam, clipped short.
Tails: White or light blue dun hackle fibers or Micro
　　Fibetts, split.
Body: Black, brown, olive, or tan fur.
Hackle: Grizzly, brown, blue dun, or ginger,
　　parachute.
Note: Tie in the wing post first, then the tail and body.
After winding the parachute hackle and finishing the
head, clip the foam post short, leaving enough so you
can see the white dot on the water with a short cast.

GRIFFITH'S GNAT

Griffith's Gnat (George Griffith)
Hook: Standard dry fly, size 14 to 24.
Thread: Black 8/0 nylon.
Hackle: Grizzly, palmered over body.
Body: Peacock herl.

TRADITIONAL MIDGE ADULT

Traditional Midge Adult
Hook: Standard dry fly, size 14 to 26.
Thread: Black, brown, olive, or tan.
Tails: Grizzly, brown, blue dun, or ginger hackle
　　fibers.
Body: Muskrat, brown, olive, or tan fur, or working
　　thread.
Hackle: Grizzly, brown, blue dun, or ginger.

Cluster Midge (Dave Hughes)
Hook: Standard dry fly, size 14 to 20.
Thread: Black, olive, or tan 8/0 nylon.

Wings: Grizzly, blue dun, or ginger hackle tips, upright and divided.

Tails: Grizzly, blue dun, or ginger hackle fibers.

Body hackle: Grizzly, blue dun, or ginger, one size undersized, palmered over body.

Body: Muskrat, olive, or tan fur, or working thread.

Hackle: Grizzly, blue dun, or ginger.

CLUSTER MIDGE

Syl's Midge (Sylvester Nemes)

Hook: Standard dry fly, size 16 to 18.

Thread: Black 8/0 nylon.

Body: Peacock herl.

Hackle: Gray partridge, one turn.

SYL'S MIDGE

■Presentation

For rising pupae on stillwaters, use weighted flies and rig with a long leader, 15 to 25 feet. About one third should be fine tippet, 5X or 6X. The line should be a floater. Cast long, let the fly sink for at least 30 seconds to a minute or more, then begin a creeping hand-twist retrieve that barely moves the fly. The object is to let it hang in the mid-depths. Keep a close eye on the line tip. You'll rarely feel a take in this kind of fishing. You'll probably miss more trout than you hook, but that is better than not hooking any. You can also rig

with a strike indicator on the leader 10 to 15 feet above a weighted midge pupal pattern. Cast out, let the fly sink, then watch the indicator patiently for any movement.

For pupae stuck just beneath the surface film, use a floating line and a 12- to 15-foot leader with a long, fine tippet. Dress the leader to the tippet knot with dry-fly floatant. Cast long and let the fly simply sit if you've got the discipline to do so. I don't, so I employ an idle hand-twist and probably reduce the number of takes I get.

Rig emergers and dry flies as you would any tiny fly for dry-fly fishing. Be sure your tippet is fine enough for the size fly you're using and not shorter than two feet. Fish the fly without movement in lakes, dead-drift on moving water. I often use a larger dry fly as an indicator if the emerger or dry fly I'm fishing is size 18 or smaller.

Fish Syl's Midge on the downstream swing through rising trout, just as you would any wet fly. If you feel a tug, don't set the hook. You'll break the fine tippet needed to fish the fly right. Merely lift the rod tip to engage the trout. That is beneficial advice no matter what midge dressing you're using: always set the hook gently. Some of the trout that sip these tiny flies will be far from small.

CHAPTER 3

LITTLE OLIVES

Order: Ephemeroptera
Family: Baetidae
Genus: *Baetis*
Species: *tricaudatus, bicaudatus,* others

LITTLE OLIVES, ALSO CALLED BLUE-WINGED OLIVES OR just olives, are among the smallest Western mayflies, but in my opinion the most important of them. They hatch for several weeks, or even months, every season. Their hatches can go on for hours each day when conditions are right, which means when the weather is lousy. Trout seem to consider them candy. When little olives are out, trout usually feed selectively on them, and ignore everything else. They are often the cause of masking hatches, where you see some large insect but cannot catch anything on its imitation. Trout will sip the tiny olives, which can be almost invisible, and ignore the larger insects that you are busy imitating.

Baetis species have incomplete metamorphosis, but have the added dun stage, unique to mayflies, between the aquatic nymph and the sexually mature spinner, which is the true adult. The dun, newly hatched and forced to ride the surface currents until its wings dry and it can fly, is the most important stage to trout fishermen. The emerger, stuck half in and half out of the nymphal shuck and pinned in the surface film, is also important. The nymph stage prompts a lot of feeding by trout, but it isn't usually selective feeding. However, *Baetis* nymphs are so abundant in favorable habitat that you'll rarely go wrong trying a tiny Pheasant Tail in waters where little olives are expected to hatch sometime later in the day. I have read of the importance of *Baetis* spinner falls, but have not discovered them descending to the water in such numbers that I've found it necessary to match them very often in my own fishing. I do not list dressings for them.

Baetis are distributed in nearly every moving water, all across the West. They do not live in lakes. Rocky and fast freestone streams have populations that are heavy enough to prompt selective feeding on occasion, especially along the quiet edges and in backwaters and eddies. The myriad of micro-niches found in the stable flows of meadow streams, spring creeks, and tailwaters prompt the heaviest hatches. *Baetis* nymphs are swimmers. They dart about in rooted vegetation, feeding on the layer of diatoms and algae that grows there. They also browse the thin layer of vegetative matter on bottom stones in freestone streams, which is why you find their populations nearly everywhere you fish, but slightly less dense where tiny, quiet niches are not as numerous.

Little olives hatch in open water. The nymph swims to the surface, penetrates the film with the top of its back, and splits open. The dun extracts itself from the nymphal shuck with a peristaltic movement, lofts its wings into the open air, and will sometimes stand on the cast shuck as on a raft or, more often, leave the shuck and ride the surface on its extended legs and the bottom of its body. As soon as the wings are dry enough to fly, the insect lifts off and heads toward streamside vegetation.

The surface film is a barrier and causes emerger opportunities, as I mentioned about midges, only with very small insects. I would guess that *Baetis* and midges between them make up more than half of all emerger fishing. If they hatch on smooth flows, say of a spring creek flat or the edge current of a freestone stream where the surface film is unbroken, the moment of emergence can be extended. Trout seem to be aware of this. They often key on struggling *Baetis* emergers rather than fully formed duns. This will not happen in riffles or runs where the surface is rough and the film is broken. Imitations of emergers are important on the kinds of water where *Baetis* are also important: on smooth flows.

Little olive hatches start as early as February on many Western trout streams, especially tailwaters that are somewhat warmed by their release from the depths of reservoirs. Hatches persist through March, April, and May, making *Baetis* an important hatch on waters that fish well before runoff begins. Hatches are not as frequent or consistent through the warm summer months. But little olives, like midges, have more than one generation per year. Their hatches pick up again when the weather begins to cool in fall. In September and October, when nearly all other aquatic insects have emerged and are back in the egg stage or early nymphal instars, and when terrestrial insects have diminished in both numbers and activity, *Baetis* hatches become abundant and important again. They continue to come off into November, and can be important on waters open all through winter.

Daily hatches of little olives tend to arise during the warmest hours of each day, especially in the early and late parts of their season. In February and March, the hatch might begin at 1:00 in the afternoon and continue until 3:00 or 4:00. In April and May the hatch might begin as early as 10:00 and trickle off until late afternoon in numbers sufficient to keep trout working the surface selectively. In autumn the hatches return to the warmest hours of the day, beginning in early afternoon.

At any time of year the hatch will last longer if the weather is cloudy and even rainy. The hatch will be shortened into a half hour to an hour or so if the sun is out and bright. My fishing friends and I often glance at the sky and say, "It's a *Baetis* day," and need talk about the weather no more than that. We know it's going to be gloomy, but the gloom will not extend to the fishing. *Baetis* weather is the kind that keeps many fly fishermen indoors, tinkering with tackle when they should be out tiffing with trout.

■ Recognition

Little olive nymphs are swimmers, with the streamlined, torpedo shape adapted to that function. They generally have two long fringed outer tails and a shorter center tail. *B. bicaudatus* has just a stub at the center tail position. The gills of the natural are small plate-like extensions to each side from the back of the abdominal segments. The antennae are long and slender.

Little olive duns are small, averaging size 18 or 20. They have two tails, slender and elongated abdomens that are one or two shades lighter in color on the underside than on the back. The thorax is bunched with muscles to propel the wings. The hindwings are tiny and eliptical, the key identifying characteristic of the duns. The eyes of the males are divided into two lobes and extended upward on top, in entomological terms called *turbinate* eyes. The duns vary from a dark olive that is almost black to an average specimen with a pale gray wing and pale olive body.

LITTLE OLIVE NYMPH

■ Key Characteristics

Nymphs: Torpedo shape.

Short or absent center tail.

Single gill plates on abdominal segments.

Antennae more than twice as long as width of head.

Size 16 to 24.

Color: Varies from dark brown to light tannish olive.

Duns: Two tails.

Tiny and elliptical hindwing.

Turbinate eyes in male.

Size from 16 to 24.

Color: Dark olive to pale grayish or tannish olive.

LITTLE OLIVE DUN

■ Imitation

The Pheasant Tail Nymph is standard for the nymph of the little olive. You will do well to fish it as a dropper beneath your emerger or dry fly in the early stages of a *Baetis* hatch, or all the way through the hatch if it continues to produce. I often fish it on a strike indicator and split-shot rig deep in waters with heavy populations of little olives, especially in the hours before a hatch. It is an excellent searching pattern any time you fish waters with hatches of little olives, even given its tiny size.

I have had uncommonly good luck fishing an olive version of the Sangre de Cristo Midge as an emerger during little olive hatches. I'll offer that dressing here, along with the standard emerger, the Little Olive Sparkle Dun, a Craig Mathews pattern based on the comparadun style, but with Antron yarn added at the stern to represent the trailing shuck. Given one pattern to fish during the *Baetis* hatch, this Sparkle Dun would likely be my choice. It imitates both the emerger and the fully formed dun. I use the Sparkle Dun, René Harrop's Little Olive Hairwing Dun, or an Olive Burned-wing Dun to imitate the winged dun.

I once had the theory that you could match any hatch with a single dressing if you could find the precise one. I now know that is not true. I would not be comfortable fishing through a *Baetis* hatch without all of the pattern styles listed below, the duns in an average olive color, in sizes 18 and 20. I tie other colors and sizes when I find that I need them for a specific *Baetis* hatch, which happens often enough that I'm usually armed with little olive dressings in several shades.

PHEASANT TAIL

Pheasant Tail (Frank Sawyer)
Hook: 1X long, size 16 to 20.
Thread: Brown 6/0 or 8/0 nylon.
Tails: Pheasant tail fibers.
Abdomen: Pheasant tail herl counter-wound with copper wire.
Wing case: Pheasant tail fibers.
Thorax: Pheasant tail fibers.
Legs: Tips of wing case fibers.

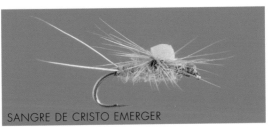
SANGRE DE CRISTO EMERGER

Sangre de Cristo Emerger
Hook: Standard dry fly, size 16 to 20.
Thread: Olive 8/0 nylon.
Wing post: Yellow closed-cell foam, clipped short after winding hackle.
Tails: White hackle fibers or Micro Fibetts, split.
Body: Olive fur or synthetic dubbing.
Hackle: Medium blue dun, parachute.

Little Olive Sparkle Dun (Craig Mathews)
Hook: Standard dry fly, size 16 to 24.

LITTLE OLIVE SPARKLE DUN

Thread: Olive 8/0 nylon.
Wing: Natural tan comparadun deer hair, in 160 degree arc.
Tail: Olive Z-lon.
Body: Olive fur or synthetic dubbing.

LITTLE OLIVE HARROP HAIRWING DUN

Little Olive Harrop Hairwing Dun (René Harrop)

Hook: Standard dry fly, size 16 to 24.
Thread: Olive 8/0 nylon.
Tails: White hackle fibers or Micro Fibetts, split.
Body: Olive fur or synthetic dubbing.
Hackle: Medium blue dun, five turns spread over thorax area, clipped on bottom.
Wing: Natural tan or gray dyed yearling elk.
Head: Butts of hair wing, clipped short.

Little Olive Burned-wing Dun

Hook: Standard dry fly, size 16 to 24.
Thread: Olive 8/0 nylon.
Wings: Blue dun hen hackles, paired and burned to proper size and shape.
Tails: White hackle fibers or Micro Fibetts, split.
Body: Olive fur or synthetic dubbing.
Hackle: Blue dun, wound parachute around wing stems.
Note: If you pair hen hackles and trim them to shape with scissors rather than using a form and burning

LITTLE OLIVE BURNED–WING DUN

them to shape, your fly is a Cutwing Dun instead of a Burned-wing Dun, which amounts to the same thing in the eyes of the trout.

■ Presentation

Imitating little olives in either the emerger or dun stages is very demanding fishing. Your tackle should be light. My standard presentation rod is a 4-weight. If you're into 2- and 3-weights, this is the time to use them.

Leaders should be 10 to 14 feet long, with two to three feet of that being tippet. I usually fish 6X for little olives, but you can get away with 5X in wind or over somewhat dirty water which you can get during early hatches. I always regret the rare need for 7X, most often considering it more an affectation than a necessity. When you hook the kind of trout that often sip *Baetis*, especially on such heavily fished waters as the Henry's Fork of the Snake, Bighorn, or Deschutes, 7X will not keep you attached to the trout you'll often hook.

The water over which you cast these small dressings will almost always be fairly smooth. In such situations, the cross-stream reach cast or downstream wiggle cast show the fly to the trout ahead of the line and leader. You will engage far more trout with these casts than you will by wading into position downstream from the trout and casting upstream to them. If a downstream approach is all that the water allows, then make your presentation upstream and across to the fish rather than directly upstream, so that your line and leader do not cross the fish in the air or on the water.

Always do your best to set the fly onto the water delicately. Do not lay the line and leader out precisely straight. Some slack allows the fly a more natural float. You'll be surprised how often any of the listed flies will fool fish feeding on little olives so long as you get your presentation just right.

CHAPTER 4

WESTERN MARCH BROWNS

Order: Ephemeroptera
Family: Heptageniidae
Genus: *Rhithrogena*
Species: *morrisoni, hageni*

THE WESTERN MARCH BROWN HATCH IS THE FIRST hatch of large insects in the typical Western trout season. These early mayflies are size 12, sometimes even 10, though at times size 14. They're always big enough to catch your attention, and that of the trout. They come off in great numbers, sometimes condensed into just an hour, covering the water and filling the air with flying duns. When March browns are available, trout are suddenly selective, and will ignore anything that is not a good match for them.

Like all mayflies, March browns have an incomplete metamorphosis, with the important dun stage between the nymph and mature spinner. The nymphs are flattened in aspect and catagorized as *clingers*, adapted to sprawling in the very thin layer of fast water that is slowed by friction in its passage over bottom stones. They live in riffles and runs. Many of them are knocked loose by the current and taken by trout, but this kind of bottom activity does not prompt selective feeding, at least in my experience. A size 12 to 14 Gold Ribbed Hare's Ear or a Pheasant Tail Nymph tied a bit portly will take trout feeding opportunistically on them along with other insects on the bottom.

The most important stage of the March brown is the dun, which takes some time to dry its large wings, especially when it hatches in the typical inclement weather of spring. The nymphs migrate to the edges of their fast-water habitat before risking the swim to the top for emergence at the surface. Most specimens make the transformation from nymph to dun in the film, in common mayfly fashion. A percentage, however, split out of the nymphal skin while still a few inches deep, and complete the trip to the surface as winged duns. These are a tangle of wings and legs, all activated by the current, and are very vulnerable to trout. A March Brown Flymph wet fly, fished on the swing through rising trout, will often take more trout than a dry fly fished on the surface. However, this is the first opportunity of the year to fish big dry flies to actively feeding and selective trout. The dry fly is the preferred method for most folks who fish this early hatch.

March browns are sprinkled in waters through the center tier of Western states. They are an important early hatch on coastal and Cascade Mountain streams in Washington and Oregon. They hatch a few weeks later in the higher-elevation streams of Idaho and Montana. They can also be important in the tumbling mountain streams of Colorado and Wyoming. Their importance dwindles as you move both south and north of these states.

Typical March brown nymphal habitat is rough water, riffles and runs in freestone streams. However, I've fished over excellent hatches of *R. hageni* on the Henry's Fork of the Snake, above the Railroad Ranch section, where the water is fast over a gravel bottom but is fairly smooth on top. You don't find many heavy populations in spring creeks or tailwaters, though they can be found in some numbers wherever the water is well oxygenated and the bottom is broken rock rather than silt or solid bedrock. The pastoral streams in the Willamette Valley of Oregon have the heaviest hatches of March browns that I've encountered. The water there has plenty of riffles and long runs. The bottom is always composed of rounded and polished stones, with lots of the kinds of niches that these clinger nymphs prefer.

Hatches on coast state streams begin in late February after a mild winter, in early March if the weather has been cold. Inland and at higher elevations in the Cascades and the Rockies, hatches begin in April, May, and even as late as June. March browns continue to come off almost daily for a month to six weeks. Daily emergence, typical of spring hatches, happens during the warmest part of the day. Early in the hatch, duns begin showing on top sometime between 1:00 and 2:00 in the afternoon. Later in the hatch they might begin to emerge as early as 10:30 or 11:00 in the morning. If the sun is bright, I've seen the hatch begin and end within a short span of forty-five minutes. About the time you figure out what to do about it, the hatch is over. On a more typical cloudy, blustery day, the hatch will last two to three hours. It usually begins and ends somewhat abruptly. Trout are feeding greedily, then suddenly no insects are around and the trout are off. When that happens it's wise to recall that many duns do not make it to the surface. Trout continue to feed subsurface on cripples. A March Brown Flymph fished on the swing will often take them for an extra hour or more.

■ Recognition

I'll not list the Western March brown nymph because trout are not selective to it along the bottom. When you fish a wet fly, just subsurface, you're actually imitating the dun after it has escaped the nymphal shuck. Since it is a disheveled creature at this stage of its life, your wet fly does not need to be anything like a precise imitation.

The dun is a large one, not easily mistaken for anything else that hatches at the same time of year. It has two tails, a fairly robust body, with the back a tannish brown to wine color, the underside's lighter tan with some olive mixed in. The forewings are large and mottled brown by their venetion. The hindwing is quite large; its shape echoes in miniature the shape of the main sail. The head of the dun is flattened, a reflection of the broad shape of the clinger nymph from which it emerges. The antennae, as on all mayfly duns, are very short.

■ Key Characteristics

Dun: Two tails about body length.
Wide, flattened head.
Mottled wings.
Size 12 to 14.
Color: Tannish brown to wine body, with some olive on the underside.

WESTERN MARCH BROWN DUN

■ Imitation

Rick Hafele, co-author of *Western Hatches* and an expert on the Western March brown hatch, worked out the March Brown Flymph to imitate the dun in its transitional stage beneath the surface. This dressing can account for as many trout during a hatch as any dry fished on the surface. It can also be used to extend the time that you're engaged with fish after the hatch. It is well worth tying and carrying.

The key factor to consider when selecting dry flies to match the mature, floating dun is the nymph's habit of migrating to the edges of fast water before swimming to the surface for emergence. The nymphs live in the kind of water where a heavily hackled pattern would be needed to fish the surface. After the nymphs move to quieter water, most duns arrive at the surface on water that is somewhat smooth but very close to rough water: At the edges of riffles and runs, in the softer water where a riffle tails out, or on the slick tailout upstream from the rough water of a riffle. Your March brown dun dressings should be more imitative, with less need for flotation, than you'd imagine from the habitat of the nymphs from which they arise.

Given that it is always wise to have some options to offer trout if they refuse what you try first, I usually carry March Brown Comparaduns, Bob Borden's March Brown Parachutes, and René Harrop's Cinnamon Hairwing Duns.

MARCH BROWN FLYMPH

March Brown Flymph (Rick Hafele)
Hook: 2X heavy, size 12 to 14.
Thread: Red 6/0 nylon or crimson red silk.
Tails: 2 or 3 pheasant tail fibers.
Body: Hare's mask fur spun on loop of working thread.
Hackle: Brown or furnace hen.
Note: Wax your working thread well and apply the body fur loosely to it. Then capture the fur in a dubbing loop, and twist it so the fur is loose and spiky, but durable when wound on the hook.

MARCH BROWN COMPARADUN

March Brown Comparadun (Richard Bunse)
Hook: Standard dry fly, size 12 to 14.

Thread: Tan 6/0 nylon.
Wing: Natural tan deer hair in 160 degree arc over body.
Tails: Brown hackle fibers, split.
Body: Tannish olive fur or synthetic dubbing.

MARCH BROWN PARACHUTE

March Brown Parachute (Robert Borden)
Hook: Standard dry fly, size 12 to 14.
Thread: Tan 6/0 nylon.
Wing post: Natural brown deer hair.
Tails: Brown hackle fibers, split.
Body: Hareline Dubbin' #32, Olive Tan.
Hackle: Brown, parachute.

CINNAMON HAIRWING DUN

Cinnamon Hairwing Dun (René Harrop)
Hook: Standard dry fly, size 12 to 14.
Thread: Tan 6/0 nylon.
Tails: Brown hackle fibers, split.
Body: Cinammon fur or synthetic dubbing.
Hackle: Brown, five turns spaced over thorax area, clipped on bottom.
Wing: Natural brown deer hair.
Head: Butts of deer hair wing clipped short.

■ Presentation

Rig for the Flymph or the dry fly in the same way, with a floating line, leader around ten feet long, and a two-

foot tippet of 4X or 5X. Fish the wet fly on the swing, by casting at an angle down and across the current, then letting the fly swim slowly down and around. You might find it necessary to give it a tug the instant it lands to pull it under the water. If it planes in the surface, trout will ignore it. Cast it into the rough water of the riffle or run, and let it swing from there into slow water. Most of your hits will happen just as the fly swings out of the fast water across the seam into slow water. Let it hang in this slower water for a few seconds before picking it up for the next cast and swing.

There are no dramatic tricks to fishing the dry fly. If you're casting over a riffle or run where trout are rising, it will not alarm the trout to fish the fly on an upstream cast. Be sure to get a good drift right down the seam between fast water and slow. If duns are emerging on fairly smooth water, use the reach cast or downstream wiggle cast to present the fly ahead of the line and leader.

Because the Western March brown is a freestone stream insect, and emerges in or near rough water, there is a tendency to treat it lightly, fishing with searching patterns that are not quite like it, using heavy lines, thick leaders, and slightly sloppy presentation techniques. Avoid this mistake. Fish the hatch with imitative patterns and all the delicacy you can achieve, and you'll be surprised at how your success increases.

CHAPTER 5

SPECKLE-WING QUILLS

Order: Ephemeroptera
Family: Baetidae
Genus: *Callibaetis*
Species: *pacifica, coloradensis, nigritus,* others

SPECKLE-WING QUILLS, IN THE GENUS *CALLIBAETIS*, are stillwater insects. They are found in fishable and important populations in almost every lake and pond in all Western states and provinces. A few populations live in spring creeks where the flows are modest and bottoms heavy with rooted weed beds. Silver Creek in Idaho springs to mind, as does the Henry's Fork of the Snake. Don't discount their presence in such waters, because they prompt selective feeding wherever they hatch. But speckle-wing quills are found most often in lakes and ponds, where they are almost always the most important mayfly hatch of the stillwater season.

Callibaetis nymphs are swimmers, closely related to *Baetis*. They live in weed beds and along the bottom wherever it has sufficient photosynthetic growth to sustain them. When you look for the presence of these insects in stillwaters, consider the limits of light penetration. Where the water is clear and light strikes down to the bottom in the depths, sometimes reaching the bottom 25 to 30 feet deep in alpine lakes, you'll find rooted weed beds and *Callibaetis* nymphs. Where the water is opaque, say in a wind-stirred desert lake with a silt bottom, light penetrates to the bottom at a maximum depth of just ten to fifteen feet. That's how deep you'll find weed growth and populations of these nymphs.

Callibaetis nymphs swim in and around vegetation, browsing on leaves and winnowing diatoms and algae off the stems. They're taken by trout during this stage of their long growth, but it's probable they're taken most often opportunistically, along with a lot of other insects and crustaceans, rather than selectively.

When mature and ready for emergence, speckle-wing quill nymphs swim boldly to the surface. They are size 12 to 16, and have enough momentum and mass to penetrate the surface film without delay. The nymphal skin splits along the back, the dun extrudes itself and escapes into the air as soon as its wings are dry. On a calm and warm day this can be almost instantly. On a windy and wet day the dun might be stranded sitting on the surface for a minute or more. Duns fly slowly to lakeside vegetation. In a day or two they molt to spinners. Male speckle-wings gather in afternoon and evening swarms, dancing gracefully up and down over the water. Females fly into the swarm, mate, and return to vegatation to let the eggs mature before laying them.

Trout give the appearance of feeding selectively on floating duns when they're present, but this can be misleading. Stomach samples I've taken over the years always reveal ten to twelve nymphs present for every dun, indicating the nymphs are taken before, and continue to be taken, during the hatch. I prefer to fish dries, matching the dun, when trout feed on the surface. But fishing a nymph through the hatch, or dangling a nymph on a 20-inch dropper behind a dry dun dressing, will account for a lot of takes, often more than fishing the dun alone.

I've seen times when trout ignored spent spinners on the water. I've seen other times when they were selective to them, and would not take anything but an exact imitation. In the first edition of this book, I declared it unnecessary to carry imitations for speckle-wing quill spinners. Since then I've learned never to fish a lake or pond without them.

The seasonal importance of speckle-wings begins in early spring, as soon as the sun begins to warm waters that do not freeze over, soon after ice-out on waters that do freeze. The first emergence in the coastal region and the southern tier of states begins in April and May. In the Rockies it recedes to June or even July, depending on elevation. Speckle-wings usually have three generations per year in each water where they emerge. The second hatch comes off about two months behind the first, the third six weeks or so behind that. It is almost impossible to pin down emergence dates that work for all waters, because the West is so varied in latitude and elevation. However, each lake has a consistent pattern repeated from year to year. On my home lakes the speckle-wing hatch begins in late April or early May and lasts three weeks to a month, tapers off until a second peak surges up in late June and July and lasts three or four weeks, then enjoys another resurgence that lasts most of September.

It's important to know that individuals in each of these generations are a size smaller than those in the one before it. If the hatch begins in spring at size 12, which is most common, the insects will be size 14 in summer, size 16 in fall. The same dressing works, but if you fail to reduce its size you'll fail to fool trout.

The daily hatch cycle begins in late morning with increased activity of nymphs. Emergence of duns in early spring begins in the warmest part of the day, just after noon, and might last only an hour on a bright day, three to four hours on a gloomy, overcast day. The hatch moves to late morning during the midsummer season, then back to the warmest part of the day again in fall.

Spinners usually begin to dance over the lake toward the tail end of the daily emergence of duns, in early to late afternoon. Spinners continue to dance far into the afternoon and evening. The spinners you see in the air are males, waiting for females to arrive. You want to pluck your sample for imitation off the water, where the spent females lie. Those are the spinners on which trout feed.

■ Recognition

Callibaetis nymphs are streamlined like all swimmer mayflies. They have three fringed tails of equal length and large gills on the abdominal segments. The first few gills have small recurved flaps that make them appear to be doubled. Speckle-wing nymphs have long antennae, which separate them from *Siphlonurus* nymphs, scattered populations of which also live in lakes and have very short antennae. Speckle-wing nymphs are size 12 to 16. Their colors vary from gray to green to brown.

Speckle-wing duns have two tails, slender abdomens that are generally tan to brownish on the back but lighter on the underside, with some olive mixed in. Always turn a mayfly dun upside down and look at it from the bottom before choosing the color of your imitation. The forewings are spotted, the hind-wings are small and eliptical like those of the related *Baetis*. The eyes of the males are split and turbinate. Size is 12 to 16.

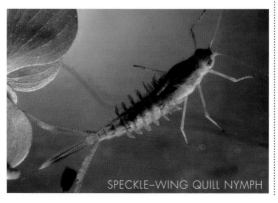

SPECKLE-WING QUILL NYMPH

Female spinners have two tails, slender grayish bodies with distinct segmentation, distinctly spotted forewings, and the same elliptical hindwing as the dun.

■ Key Characteristics

Nymph: Three fringed tails.
Recurved gills on segments 1 to 4 or 1 to 7.
Antennae longer than two times width of head.
Size 12 to 16.
Color: Green, grayish or tannish green, to brown.

Dun: Two tails.
Mottled forewings.
Small, elliptical hindwings.
Male eyes turbinate.
Size 12 to 16.
Color: Tan to brown with olive mixed on underside.

Spinner: Two tails.
Spotted forewings.
Small, elliptical hindwings.
Male eyes turbinate.
Size 12 to 18.
Color: Gray to wine red.

SPECKLE-WING QUILL SPINNER

■ Imitation

It is important to carry imitations of all three stages of
the speckle-wing quills. You'll use nymphs in the hours
before a hatch, fish duns during selective feeding
throughout the hatch, perhaps with a nymph dressing
on a dropper, and fish a spinner dressing when clouds
of males fill the air and it's obvious that trout feed on
females falling spent to the water. Nymph patterns
should be tied slender, and weighted slightly, if at all.
They'll be fished shallow. The dun patterns need no
flotation, so you can choose dressings that show the
silhouette of the body lowered into the surface film.
Spinner dressings should be tied spent. I've come to
prefer an A. K. Best quill body dressing, from his book
A. K.'s Fly Box (Lyons & Burford, 1996) for the distinct
segmentation the quill body gives.

FLASHBACK PHEASANT TAIL

Flashback Pheasant Tail
Hook: 1X long, size 12 to 16.
Weight: 15 to 20 turns of undersized lead wire,
   optional.
Thread: Brown 6/0 or 8/0 nylon.
Tails: Pheasant tail fibers.
Ribbing: Fine gold wire, counterwound over body.
Abdomen: Pheasant tail herl.
Wing case: Pearlescent Flashabou.
Thorax: Pheasant tail fibers.
Legs: Tips of thorax fibers.

CALLIBAETIS NYMPH

Callibaetis Nymph
Hook: 1X long, size 12 to 16.
Weight: 15 to 20 turns of undersized lead wire,
   optional.
Thread: Olive 6/0 or 8/0 nylon.
Tails: Olive-dyed partridge fibers.

Body: Tannish olive fur dubbing.
Wing case: Olive dyed partridge fibers.
Legs: Tips of wing case fibers.

CALLIBAETIS COMPARADUN

Callibaetis **Comparadun** (Al Caucci and Bob Nastasi)

Hook: Standard dry fly, size 12 to 16.
Thread: Olive 6/0 or 8/0 nylon.
Wing: Natural tan comparadun deer hair.
Tails: White hackle fibers or Micro Fibetts, split.
Body: Tannish olive fur or synthetic dubbing.

CALLIBAETIS HAIRWING DUN

Callibaetis **Hairwing Dun** (René Harrop)

Hook: Standard dry fly, size 12 to 16.
Thread: Olive 6/0 or 8/0 nylon.
Tails: White hackle fibers or Micro Fibetts, split.
Body: Tannish olive fur or synthetic dubbing.
Hackle: Blue dun, five turns over thorax area, clipped on bottom.
Wing: Natural tan yearling elk hair.
Head: Butts of hair wing, clipped short.

Callibaetis **Quill Spinner** (A. K. Best)

Hook: Standard dry fly, size 12 to 18.
Thread: Gray 6/0 or 8/0 nylon.
Tails: Blue dun hackle fibers, split.
Body: Gray-dyed hackle feather stem.
Wings: Grizzly hackle, tied spent.
Thorax: Gray fur or synthetic.

CALLIBAETIS QUILL SPINNER

■ Presentation

Rig to fish all three stages—nymph, dun, and spinner—
with a floating line and a 10- to 14-foot leader. Be sure
the tippet is at least two to three feet long before you
tie on a fly and begin fishing. If you're going to fish a
nymph, take time to carefully stretch your leader until
it is as straight as you can get it. If it is coiled in the
water, a trout can take your fly and run two or three
feet with it before you get the news about it. A leader
that is not straightened is the biggest mistake you can
make when fishing nymphs in stillwaters. Fish the
nymph shallow. Cast out, let it sink for a short time,
retrieve with a slow hand-twist. Alternate this with a
few strips that scoot the nymph right along, as if it's
swimming toward the top for emergence.

Fish the duns on the sit, as you do most dry flies
on still waters. When fishing to a pod of rising trout,
cast to those rises at the near edge of the pod to keep
from frightening the rest of the fish. If you're casting
to a single rising trout, cast as near to the latest rise as
you can. If trout are rising somewhat consistently in a
small area, cast to that area and let the fly rest rather
than picking it up and casting it into every new rise
ring. Don't put the trout down. Keep an eye on the fly.
My biggest problem fishing dry flies during this hatch
is casting out, waiting for a trout to come to the fly,
then getting caught staring off toward Kansas when a
trout slips up and whacks it.

If you can pinpoint the direction of travel of a
cruising trout, calculate the spot of the projected next
rise. Set the fly there early and hold on while the trout
appproaches. This is the worst kind of rise to antici-
pate. I always set the hook so hard when it comes that
I break off if the trout has any size at all.

I hope you're not as quick on the trigger as I am.

CHAPTER 6

AMERICAN GRANNOMS

Order: Trichoptera
Family: Brachycentridae
Genus: *Brachycentrus*
Species: *americanus, occidentalis*

THESE SMALL, DARK CADDISFLIES ARE PRESENT IN nearly every Western trout stream. They are important at times in most of them. Two species dominate the hatch, *B. occidentalis* in spring and *B. americanus* in late summer and fall. The early hatch is often called the Mother's Day caddis, especially in the Yellowstone region. The later hatch is referred to as the American grannom. They are both widespread, and too similar for easy separation except in terms of timing of the hatches.

Both species are small, generally size 16 to 18, though in the early season as large as size 14. Both species have dark wings, brown or gray, that sometimes look black when observed from anything but close distance. Their bodies are dark green, commonly so dark they also appear to be black until you take a close look.

Sylvester Nemes, in his book *Soft-Hackled Fly Imitations* (Stackpole, 1991), notes that the Mother's Day caddis hatch on his home waters, in the Yellowstone area, comes off in such numbers that they often form drifting rafts in the days just before runoff begins in early May. I've seen these small caddis prompt selective feeding on the Yellowstone River until runoff knocked it out. Then the same hatch began emerging on the Madison River below Beartrap Canyon, where runoff was not a problem.

The American grannom is a fall hatch on many important Western trout streams. I've encountered it on Montana's Bighorn River in excellent numbers in September, hatching on smooth currents, prompting big selective browns to sip nearsightedly. On many rivers the hatch begins in August and goes on for several weeks, causing selective feeding almost every day. One of the two species hatches on almost every stream at some time during the season, though not always in such numbers that trout will feed selectively on them.

Brachycentrus larvae build square cases from wood debris. The case looks as if a fine woodworker built dozens of tiny window frames in descending sizes, then glued them together to form a tube. Trout eat the larvae often, case and all, but not selectively.

Pupation occurs inside the sealed larval case. Larvae often gather in colonies on the same submerged stone. When mature a few weeks later, the pupae cut free and swim to the surface. I've not taken stomach samples during these early-afternoon hatches, but suspect that far more pupae are taken than adults.

Unlike most caddisflies, the adults drift on the surface for some time before flying away. At times the water is peppered with tiny drifting caddis. If the wind is blowing, matts of them get blown together and drift along the edges and sometimes pile up against the shore. Trout sip them in singles or loft noses to accept them by the bunch. It's impossible to imitate them in bunches, but it's important to have dressings for pupae and for single adults.

These vegetation-cased caddis are adapted to peaceful flows, which is why you find them important most often in larger, more mature, and therefore slower rivers. The hatch will be important on gentle runs and flats, not riffles and cascades. I have found fish feeding selectively to them most often where the water has a steady but gentle flow in the edge currents within two to ten feet of the bank.

I have fished the Mother's Day caddis most often in May, the American grannoms in September. But I know there are fishable spring hatches in April and June, late hatches in August through October. It's likely that air and water temperature control their emergence dates, and that you might encounter one of the species of *Brachycentrus* in any month, somewhere in the West.

Daily emergence in the cold spring months tends toward the warmest part of each day, in early to mid-afternoon. In late summer and fall, American grannoms tend to start emerging in late afternoon and continue on into the evening unless the weather is cold. Both hatches usually go on for several hours, keeping trout up and interested the entire time. Many individuals fail to make it into the winged adult stage. They linger on or under the water, especially if the weather is cold and raining. Trout will keep feeding on them, and will continue to take flies that imitate them, until evening cold or darkness drives you from the water.

■ Recognition

Because I have not killed fish during this hatch, and prefer not to use stomach pumps, I have not collected Mother's Day caddis or American grannom pupae. The scant information on them reports them to be tan or green, most often the latter, with distinct stripes on the sides. Their heads and wing pads are dark brown, the wing pads almost black when the insect is mature and emerging. The adults have dark brown to dark gray wings. Their abdomens are usually a dark olive that is almost black.

■ Key Characteristics

Pupae: Tan or green bodies with distinct stripes.
Dark heads and wing pads.
Size 14 to 18.
Adults: Dark brown or gray wings.
Dark olive bodies.
Size 14 to 18.

AMERICAN GRANNOM ADULT

JIM SCHOLLMEYER
AMERICAN GRANNOM PUPA

■ Imitation

I recommend a couple of soft-hackle dressings for the pupae. The same dressings also resemble shipwrecked and drowned adults, which seem to be taken at least as often by trout as fully formed and floating adults. I have not checked stomachs during these hatches, but have found that a soft-hackle will take at least as many trout as a dry-fly pattern even when the trout are obviously feeding on adults adrift on the surface. I would feel comfortably armed for all *Brachycentrus* hatches with a few of Sylvester Nemes's Mother's Day Caddis Soft-Hackles, plus a half dozen traditional Starling and Herls, both tied in size 16.

A dry fly will take trout well when adults are drifting as singles. When they're present in such numbers that they form rafts, or speckle the water so densely that you cannot pick your imitation out of the mass of naturals, it's always easier to fish a wet dressing because you can then feel the take, without the need to see it.

For an imitative dry fly, I've found nothing better than Jim Schollmeyer's Deer Hair Caddis in size 16. It's wise to bear in mind that this is a hatch you can get away with mismatching at times. This is especially true in spring, during bad weather, on freestone streams. Trout will often accept an Elk Hair Caddis or small

Royal Wulff, either of which are easily separated from the naturals around them.

MOTHER'S DAY CADDIS SOFT-HACKLE

Mother's Day Caddis Soft-Hackle
(Sylvester Nemes)

Hook: Standard dry fly, size 16 to 18.
Thread: Black 8/0 nylon.
Body: Peacock herl.
Hackle: Gray partridge.
Head: Dark mole fur.
Note: Wind the partridge as hackle at the end of the body, then gather it in a bunch over the back of the fly.

Starling & Herl

Hook: Standard dry fly, size 16 to 18.
Thread: Black 8/0 nylon.
Hackle: Starling breast feather with purple sheen.
Body: Peacock herl.

STARLING & HERL

Note: Tie the hackle in first at the hook eye, by the stem, with the tip extended to the front. Twist the herl together with the thread before winding it, for durability. Finish by winding the fragile hackle back toward the body, then take three or four turns of thread through it to secure it firmly against the sharp teeth of trout. If you do not, the fly might unravel after one or two trout.

DEER HAIR CADDIS

Deer Hair Caddis (Jim Schollmeyer)

Hook: Standard dry fly, size 16 to 18.
Thread: Olive 8/0 nylon.
Hackle: Dark blue dun, palmered over body.
Body: Dark olive fur or synthetic.
Wing: Natural dun deer hair.

■ Presentation

You will occasionally encounter this hatch in conditions that allow you to fish it rather coarsely for its size. When it happens in spring on a blustery day, trout will not refuse you if you use 4X tippet, though I always use 5X or 6X. It can be an advantage to set the dry fly hard on the water if there are so many naturals around that you have trouble spotting your imitation among them. If you give your fly a hard landing you'll see it smack down among the many, and be able to single it out and follow its drift.

Most often during the hatch, when trout are selective and conditions are calm, you should fish the dry fly with a long, fine leader and all the finesse you can derive from your tackle. On smooth Bighorn or Missouri River currents in September, during the American grannom hatch, anything less will net you no trout.

Soft-hackled wet-fly dressings should be fished on short casts, down-and-across current, and be allowed to swing slowly through rising trout. Mend constantly to slow the swing. Watch your line tip where it enters the water. If it twitches or darts, set the hook. Most takes will register as sullen tugs. Restrain yourself from setting the hook hard. The size trout that feed on these small caddis will part a fine tippet if you do anything more than lift the rod gently to seat the hook.

CHAPTER 7

SALMONFLIES

Order: Plecoptera
Family: Pteronarcidae
Genus: *Pteronarcys*
Species: *californica*

THE SALMONFLY HATCH DRAWS UP THE LARGEST predatory trout in any stream where it emerges. It is usually considered the most important Western stonefly hatch, competing only with the golden stones, which are nearly as large, more widely distributed, but do not incite quite the same selective feeding by big trout. The biggest drawback of the salmonfly hatch is that heavy populations are found in only a few waters throughout the West, though most are famous rivers. A second drawback is that the hatch causes such eagerness among big trout that those rivers draw pandemonious crowds of anglers during the hatch.

Like all stoneflies, salmonflies have incomplete metamorphosis. Nymphs mature and hatch directly into adults. The adults hang around in streamside vegetation for some weeks, mate, lay their eggs, and die or are devoured by trout. There are no pupal, dun, or spinner stages to confuse the mix. Both the nymph and adult samonfly stages cause selective feeding, and are important to anglers.

Salmonfly nymphs live for three or four years, always in water that is well charged with oxygen. Most populations are in freestone streams with bouldered bottoms and lots of niches among stones. Though large, up to two inches long, the nymphs are not predaceous, but peaceful browsers. They feed on vegetation either rooted to the bottom or growing on bottom stones. Because the typical life cycle is three years, there are always first- and second-year class salmonfly nymphs available to trout in waters with good populations, even just after the hatch ends and all current year class nymphs are gone.

When mature and ready for emergence, salmonfly nymphs migrate from their mid-water habitat in riffles and runs to shore. They crawl out of the water late in the evening on cloudy days, after dark on sunny days. The nymphal skin splits down the back, and the adult slowly emerges, all on streamside rocks or vegetation. It is the patient nature of this emergence, and consequent exposure to bird predation, that causes it to happen most often under the cover of darkness.

Nymphs are most important during the migration to shore. Many of them gather in the water right along the shoreline, waiting for their time to crawl out. Trout that are scattered in lies all across a river in spring, prior to the salmonfly hatch, will follow these large and lumbering nymphs to shore and become gathered themselves in shoreline or edge lies where they're less difficult to reach with a dead-drifted nymph or salmonfly dry.

Adult salmonflies are awkward. They hang around in grasses and shrubs near and often overhanging the water. I've seen three or four of them hike out to the end of a bunchgrass blade drooping dangerously over the Deschutes. Then a couple more decide to join the convention. The grass blade collapses under their weight and all are pitched onto the water. You can imagine the greed that half a dozen insects up to a couple of inches long can create among waiting trout. That is why the largest fish leave their secure lies in deeper water to hold along the shoreline during this hatch. Big trout winnow nymphs as they migrate, then accept adults as they drop in.

While the nymph migration is still in progress, trout seem to concentrate on nymphs and often ignore adults that have already hatched. I've seen an adult salmonfly drift over the backs of trout rooting for nymphs in water a foot deep, the trout either failing to notice the struggling adult or ignoring it. When the migration has run its course, and more adults are around than nymphs are left to emerge, trout then turn their attention upward. I emphasize this because you can get a one- or two-week period when lots of adults are out, and it seems a dry fly would be best, but you won't take many fish unless you continue to fish a nymph along the bottom.

When adults become the most common fare for trout, they're usually taken right at the edges. Bank lies become the most important water when salmonfly adults are clambering awkwardly in the vegetation. You'll know when this time has arrived by the sight, and even the sound of the takes, which are like detonations.

Distribution of salmonflies is most heavy, but not restricted to, the tier of states starting with Washington and Oregon on the coast, moving inland to Idaho, then on into Montana and Wyoming. Hatches happen in states south of this and provinces to the north, but those rivers that make the salmonfly famous occur in this band: the Deschutes in Oregon, the Yakima in Washington, the South Fork and Henry's Fork of the Snake in Idaho, the Madison, Big Hole, and Yellowstone in Montana, the upper Green in Wyoming. The hatch seems to be most important in big famous rivers, though the rivers become famous in part because they have the hatch.

Seasonal importance begins in late May and early June in the coastal regions, moves to mid- and late June at higher elevations inland, and ends in early to mid-July in the high and cold waters of the Yellowstone River in and below the park.

Daily importance lasts all day for the nymphs. Trout take them whenever opportunity presents. If you fish a big imitation tumbling along the bottom, they'll accept it at any time of day. Adults are most active when the sun warms them and revs their motors. They're most awkward, and tumble most often to the water, in the first couple of hours after they begin moving around, before they're warmed enough to attain full mobility. They'll begin falling in around ten o'clock or a little later on a warm day, and continue drawing the focus of trout upward for the rest of the day. When a trout hits an adult, or your imitation, it's usually with an explosion, though I've seen big trout slip up and sip a size 6 salmonfly dry so daintily you'd not know it happened if your fly were not suddenly missing. The detonation then happens when you set the hook.

■ Recognition

Salmonfly nymphs are distinguished by their two stout and stubby tails, the absence of gills on most of the abdominal segments where all mayfly nymphs have theirs, and the presence of brushy white or grayish gills on the underside of the thorax. The key characteristic that separates salmonfly nymphs from other stoneflies is tufts of gills on the first two abdominal segments. The nymphs of the emerging year class are very large, and light to dark brown, sometimes almost black. The first- and second-year classes are much smaller, size 10 though size 16 depending on the stage of their approach to maturity.

Adults have two tails, somewhat short and stout, heavily veined wings held flat over the body, and remnants of the abdominal gills on the first two segments behind the thorax. They are large, imitated on

SALMONFLY NYMPH

size 4 to 8 hooks. They are dark brown on the back, salmon-colored on the bottom, and often have hot orange markings between the head and first thoracic segment.

SALMONFLY ADULT

■ Key Characteristics:

Nymph: Two tails.
Two tarsal claws.
Two tufts of abdominal gills.
Thoracic gill tufts.
Size 4 to 8 in the mature year class.
Color: Light to very dark brown, almost black.

Adult: Two tails.
Two tarsal claws.
Flat wings with heavy venetion.
Gill remnants on abdomen and thorax.
Size 4 to 8.
Color: Dark brown with salmon on the underside, and hot orange behind head.

■ Imitation

Nearly any big and black dressing will usually take trout feeding on salmonfly nymphs, if it's fished dead drift, tumbling along the bottom. When the naturals get knocked loose from their grip on bottom stones, which happens often during their migration, they curl into a ball to increase their sectional density, so they sink faster. As soon as they touch a stone they unfold and try to get a grip on the bottom.

I subscribe to the late Charles Brooks's theory that a salmonfly nymph should be tied in the round, so that a trout sees the same thing no matter how the fly is turned over in the water. His Brooks Stone is my favorite during the migration, and also one of my favorites as a searching pattern on large Western waters, and all around the world. Randall Kaufmann's Black Stone is the accepted dressing for the nymph on the Deschutes River.

Imitations of the adult should give a good impression of a large insect struggling on the surface. I have rarely found the need for anything more imitative than the old salmonfly standard, the Improved Sofa Pillow. But most of my fishing over this hatch has been done on the broad and brawling Deschutes, my home river. I can understand that on smoother stretches of other rivers a more exact silhouette of the natural might serve as a better taker of trout.

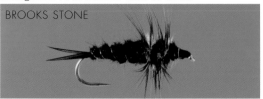

BROOKS STONE

Brooks Stone (Charles Brooks)
Hook: 3X long, size 4 to 8.
Weight: 20 to 30 turns of lead wire the diameter of the hook shank.
Thread: Black 3/0 Monocord or 6/0 nylon.
Tails: Dark goose biots, split.
Rib: Copper wire.
Abdomen: Black fur dubbing or wool yarn.
Hackle: Black hen, two wraps over thorax.
Gills: White or light gray ostrich herl, wound with hackle.
Thorax: Black fur dubbing or wool yarn.

KAUFMANN'S BLACK STONE

Kaufmann's Black Stone (Randall Kaufmann)
Hook: 6X long, size 2 to 10.
Weight: 20 to 30 turns of lead wire.
Thread: Black 6/0 nylon.
Tails: Black turkey biots, split.
Rib: Black transparent Swannundaze.
Body: 1/2 black Hare-Tron, 1/2 mix of claret, red, orange, rust, black, brown, blue, and purple Angora goat.
Wing pads: Dark turkey tail sections.
Antennae: Black turkey biots.

Improved Sofa Pillow
Hook: 3X long, size 4 to 8.
Thread: Black 6/0 nylon.
Tail: Natural elk body hair.
Rib: Brown hackle, palmered over abdomen.
Body: Burnt orange fur or synthetic.
Wing: Natural elk body hair.
Hackle: Brown saddle.

IMPROVED SOFA PILLOW

Henry's Fork Salmonfly (Mike Lawson)

Hook: 3X long, size 4 to 8.
Thread: Hot orange 6/0 nylon.
Tail: Black moose.
Hackle: Brown, palmered and clipped short.
Body: Orange fur or synthetic.
Wing: Natural dark elk hair.
Head: Moose body hair, bullet style.
Collar: Tips of head hair.

CLARK'S STONEFLY

Clark's Stonefly (Lee Clark)

Hook: 3X long, size 4 to 8.
Thread: Orange 6/0 nylon.
Body: Flat gold tinsel.
Underwing: Rust and gold macramé yarn, teased together.
Overwing: Moose body hair.
Hackle: Blue dun.

■ Presentation

Salmonfly nymph dressings should always be fished dead drift, right on the bottom. Allow them to ride up from that zone and you'll reduce the number of strikes, often to none. Get the nymph in that bottom zone, tumbling freely, and trout will usually whack it so hard you have no trouble telling about the take.

I usually rig with a floating line, large fan of yellow yarn for a strike indicator at the butt section of a 10-foot leader tapered to 3X. The salmonfly nymph itself usually has enough weight to get to the bottom, without split shot. I'll adjust the cast farther up into the current to get the nymph to sink deeper, farther out across the current if it's getting too deep, rather than add weight, if I can avoid it. If shot are needed, however, I'd rather add it than fish above the bottom.

Many folks fish these flies without the indicator, but I prefer it as a marker for the way my drift is going. I'm also not expert at noticing subtle takes without the fluff of yarn, but that reflects my lack of constant fishing with the nymph without an indicator more than any failure of the method.

The critical thing is to cast upstream far enough into the current to let the fly sink all the way to the bottom. Then mend and tend the line so the fly tumbles freely as far as possible. At the end of the drift, stop the rod and let the current lift the fly off the bottom. Many strikes will occur at that instant and you'll have no trouble noticing them. If you do not get a take, cast upstream again and get a new drift along the bottom within a foot or so of the one before it. Paint the bottom with parallel strokes of the nymph in this manner, fishing all of the water.

The dry fly is best fished dead-drift, right along the edge, especially beneath overhanging grass and branches. If the water lets you position yourself out from the bank, it's often best to fish downstream, casting the fly carefully to set it next to the edge, then tossing slack into the drift behind it to let the fly float freely downstream. If you get drag, tug the fly upstream to set up its drift again, then toss more slack behind it. You can sometimes get ten to fifteen feet of effective drift this way, right along the bank. By casting downstream rather than upstream, the fly arrives ahead of the line and leader.

If you're fishing dries by hiking the banks of a big river, as I most often do on the Deschutes, then poke the fly into all the brushy pockets you can, and get the best float you can achieve by manipulation of the drift. Creeping and crawling the banks is my favorite occupation during salmonfly time on my big home river. I enjoy the detonations I'm able to cause, though I'm not always able to land the trout that I hook.

CHAPTER 8

GOLDEN STONES

Order: Plecoptera
Family: Perlidae
Genus: *Calineuria*
Species: *californica*
Genus: *Hesperoperla*
Species: *pacifica*

GOLDEN STONES ARE SECOND IN SIZE, BUT NOT always in importance, to the giant salmonflies that precede them by a week or two, often on the same rivers. It is common for adults of the two groups to gather in the same streamside shrubs and grasses. The one hatch tapers off as the other gathers full force.

The primary species known as the golden stone is *Calineuria californica* (in fly-fishing and entomology books published before the early 1980s, listed under the old name *Acroneuria californica*). A slightly less common but still very widespread and abundant golden stone, *Hesperoperla pacifica* (old name *Acroneuria pacifica*), is sometimes called the willow fly in Colorado and other waters in the south Rocky Mountain states. The two species are so near in size, form, color, and behavior that it is not necessary to separate them when selecting imitations.

Like salmonflies, golden stones have incomplete metamorphosis, passing from nymph to adult and mating in that final form. They have a three-, and perhaps in some cases four-year life cycle. The nymphs of the year class emerging are most important when they migrate for the hatch and gather at the shoreline. Nymphs of the second year class are present in the water and are taken by trout at all times of the year. These immature nymphs are two or even three sizes smaller than those that are mature and about to emerge. The constant presence of smaller golden stone nymphs is a probable cause for the consistant success of size 12 and 14 Gold Ribbed Hare's Ear nymphs. Trout feed readily on mature golden stone nymphs, but the naturals do not migrate in the same masses as salmonfly nymphs, and it is unlikely that trout feed on golden stone nymphs as selectively as they do on salmonfly nymphs.

Golden stone nymphs are predaceous, always on the prowl among bottom stones looking for mayfly and smaller stonefly nymphs, caddis and midge larvae, and anything else they can subdue and eat. They are often knocked loose into the current, and trout are happy about it when they see it happen. If even minor numbers of these large nymphs are present in any samples you take of the stream bottom, an imitation will make an excellent searching dressing.

Preferred habitat of golden stone nymphs are rough and broken stream bottoms in fast currents, with lots of oxygen. They do their prowling and hunting in the niches among bottom stones. They are found most often in freestone streams. They are usually abundant in the same large rivers where salmonfly nymphs are important. They are far more widespread, though. You'll find good golden stone populations in the tertiary network of smaller streams and creeks in every state and province in the West.

Golden stone nymphs gather at the shoreline during the day and emerge at night by crawling out on the bank. Most salmonflies escape the nymphal skin within a few inches or a few feet of the waterline. Many golden stones hike up to fifty or 100 feet from shore and climb high up the trunks of trees before casting the nymphal skin. This takes place after dark. I've often seen salmonflies hatch on cloudy afternoons and evenings. I've never seen golden stones leave the water during daylight, though I've little doubt they do at times.

Golden stone adults hang around in bankside grasses, shrubs, and willow trees. They often drop to the water. But they're not as awkward either on vegetation or in flight as the slightly larger salmonflies. Trout do not get quite the consistent number of looks at them. However, trout drawn to the edges of any stream by the earlier and larger insects will remain in their bank lies, waiting for the arrival by water of golden stone nymphs and by accident of golden stone adults.

On a few cloudy afternoons, the mass of golden stones in the vegetation will take wing for egg-laying flights. These are rare, and far from predictable, at least in my experience. When you hit one though, it's hard to believe the numbers of insects in the air, landing on the water, being taken greedily by trout. When it happens you can move away from the shoreline and fish your imitations over explosive rises in riffles and runs: wherever trout hang out. But golden stone adult imitations are most often productive when fished at the edges.

Seasonal occurance of the golden stone hatch starts in early June in the coastal regions, at the tail end of the salmonfly hatch. It moves to late June when you get farther inland, and to early or mid-July in the Rocky Mountain states and provinces. The willow fly in Colorado has been reported to be important in September. Golden stone adults will be present for two or three weeks, scrambling around at streamside.

Daily activity begins as soon as the sun heats the air enough for the adults to become active in vegetation. When numbers are present at the edges, trout will be aware of them and on the lookout for them in bank water starting around nine or ten o'clock on sunny days, a bit later if the weather is not quite so warm. If an ovipositing flight takes place, it will probably begin around three to four in the afternoon, and go on for two or three hours.

■ Recognition

Golden stone nymphs have two somewhat stout tails, and lack gills on any abdominal segments. They have tufted thoracic gills that look like chest and armpit hair at the bases of the legs. The prominant and beautiful vermiculations on the back of the head and thoracic segments are key characteristics. The nymphs have large, strong mandibles that make them look fierce, and that separate them from less predaceous stoneflies. All stoneflies, as nymphs and adults, can be separated from mayflies by the presence of two claws rather than one at the end of each tarsal segment: two claw-like toes rather than one. Nymphs of *Hesperoperla pacifica*, sometimes called the willow fly, have two tufts of gill filaments between the tails. These look like pom poms, and make this insect unmistakable.

Golden stone adults have two tails, two tarsal claws, and wings that lie flat over the back when they're at rest. They're most easily recognized by their large size, 1 1/2 to 2 inches long, and by their golden-brown coloration. If you flip them over to look at the underside, which you should because that is the side a trout sees when it is about to whack one, you'll see that they're golden or even bright yellow on the bottom.

GOLDEN STONE NYMPH

■ Key Characteristics

Nymphs: Two tails.
Two tarsal claws.
Thoracic gill tufts.
Vermiculations on back of head and thorax.
Large, sharp mandibles.
Gill tufts between tails on *H. pacifica*.
Size 4 to 12 (including second-year class).
Color: Light to dark brown, mottled.

Adults: Two tails.
Two tarsal claws.
Wings held flat over back when at rest.
Size 6 to 8.
Color: Golden brown to dark brown; gold to bright yellow on underside of abdomen.

GOLDEN STONE ADULT

■ Imitation

If you fish Western waters, you should carry imitations for both the nymphs and adults of the golden stones. Nymph dressings make excellent searching patterns in most streams and rivers because trout are accustomed to seeing stray golden stone nymphs on the prowl. Fish are always eager to get them because of their size. A weighted golden stone nymph imitation is an excellent searching pattern in riffles, runs, and pocket water whenever nothing in particular is going on. They're important as imitative patterns if the migration of nymphs toward shore is so heavy that trout become selective to them, though this latter case will be rare, in my experience.

Patterns for adult golden stones are valuable whenever the naturals are present in any numbers. Randall Kaufmann's Stimulator, tied slightly small, is an excellent grasshopper and caddisfly imitation as well as being great for the golden stone. You won't go wrong fishing a Stimulator at the edges of any Western stream, at almost any time of year, even when no golden stones are around.

Yellow Stone Nymph (Charles Brooks)
Hook: 3X or 4X long, size 6 to 10.
Weight: 15 to 25 turns lead wire diameter of hook shank.
Thread: Brown 3/0 Monocord or 6/0 nylon.
Tails: Brown turkey biots, forked.
Rib: Gold yarn counterwound with fine gold wire.
Body: Yellowish brown wool yarn, or yellow and brown fur, mixed.
Hackle: Brown hen, two turns over thorax.
Gills: White or light gray ostrich herl, wound with hackle.

KAUFMANN'S GOLDEN STONE

Kaufmann's Golden Stone (Randall Kaufmann)
Hook: 6X long, size 8 to 12.
Weight: 15 to 25 turns of lead wire.
Thread: Brown 6/0 nylon.
Antennae: Ginger goose biots, forked.
Tails: Ginger goose biots, forked.
Rib: Amber Swannundaze.
Abdomen: 1/2 golden brown Hare-Tron, 1/2 mix of claret, amber, orange, rust, black, brown, blue, purple, and ginger Angora goat.
Wing pads: Mottled turkey sections.
Thorax and head: Same as abdomen.

Kaufmann's Stimulator (Randall Kaufmann)
Hook: 3X long, size 6 to 12.
Thread: Hot orange 6/0 nylon.

Tail: Light elk hair.
Rib: Fine gold wire, counterwound over ribbing hackle.
Ribbing hackle: Light brown, one size undersized, wound over abdomen.
Abdomen: Golden fur or synthetic.
Wing: Light elk hair.
Hackle: Grizzly, wound over thorax.
Thorax: Amber fur or synthetic.

HENRY'S FORK GOLDEN STONE

Henry's Fork Golden Stone (Mike Lawson)
Hook: 3X long, size 8 to 10.
Thread: Tan 3/0 Monocord.
Tail: Light elk hair.
Hackle: Brown, trimmed and palmered over body.
Body: Yellowish tan fur.
Wing: Light elk hair.
Head: Light tan elk hair, bullet style.
Collar: Tips of head hair.

Improved Golden Stone
Hook: 3X long, size 6 to 10.
Thread: Black 6/0 nylon.
Tail: Bleached deer body hair.
Rib: Cream or light ginger hackle, undersized, palmered.

Body: Cream yarn or fur.
Wing: Light elk hair.
Hackle: Cream or light ginger.

■ Presentation

To fish the nymph, rig for the bottom. That's the only place they live, and the only place trout find them. The best bet is around a 10- to 12-foot leader, tapered to 3X or 4X, with a large yarn or hard strike indicator fixed to the leader not far from the end of the line. Adjust the indictor up or down the leader to reach various depths. Cast high into the current, and give the fly plenty of time to sink to the bottom. Continually mend and tend your line to keep the indicator floating freely downstream, which is your best signal that the nymph is tumbling without resistance down below. Fish out each cast until the nymph lifts off the bottom at the downstream end, and make your next cast a foot or two out from the one before it. Paint every bit of bottom in this manner.

Rig for the adult on the same leader, minus the indicator. You'll want to fish it dead drift along the shoreline most often, when golden stone adults are out. You can fish upstream, and get a free drift back toward you. Or you can set up to cast downstream. Toss plenty of slack onto the water as the fly floats downstream along the edge. If the line and leader straighten, and the fly begins to drag, set up the float again by drawing the fly upstream and across the current two or three feet, then lowering the rod and dropping more slack line onto the water.

If adults are in the air for an egg-laying flight, watch where they land, and cast the large dry flies over the rises you'll see tossing spray into the air.

CHAPTER 9

WESTERN GREEN DRAKES

Order: Ephemeroptera
Family: Ephemerellidae
Genus: *Drunella*
Species: *grandis, doddsi, flavilinea,* and *coloradensis*

THE GREEN DRAKE GROUP COMPRISES THE MOST famous Western mayfly hatch, but I rate it in terms of importance behind the little olives, pale morning duns, and if you fish lakes and ponds more than a little, the speckle-wing quills. All of those, though smaller, hatch more often on more waters and over longer periods of time, prompting trout to feed selectively more often, in more places. When green drakes come off in any sort of numbers, though, they're large enough that trout key on them. You must match them or you're not going to catch many fish. Like any other insect, during their moment of most importance they're the only thing around that counts. I just don't feel that they count quite as often as some of the smaller but more abundant mayfly hatches. However, there are so many species, and they live in so many important waters, that you're bound to encounter one or another of the green drakes at some time during the trout season.

Green drakes have an incomplete metamorphosis, going through nymph, dun, and spinner stages. The nymph is eaten often, but not often selectively in my experience. I do not list a dressing specifically for them, though I suspect that a size 12 or 14 Gold Ribbed Hare's Ear is taken by a trout, it is often mistaken for a green drake nymph. I said the same thing in the last chapter about second year class golden stonefly nymphs. The Hare's Ear looks like a lot of things that trout eat, which is why it works so well.

The green drake dun is the most important stage of the hatch. It takes a long time for those large wings to dry. The newly hatched dun might ride the surface for a minute or more before launching into the air. That gives trout lots of time to look over the insect and to plot an ambush or a refusal. Spinners are large enough to be important when they fall in great numbers. I've only had that happen once or twice in my travels on Western waters. It's important when it does happen, no matter how infrequently that might be, because trout become selective to an insect so large.

Habitat for the natural nymph is any cold and well-oxygenated flowing water. Green drakes are not found in lakes or ponds. They adapt well to either cobbled bottoms or rooted vegetation, if there is sufficient oxygen in the water. The most condensed hatches I've encountered generally happen on spring creeks or tailwaters: *D. coloradensis* on Fall River in Oregon and Slough Creek in Yellowstone Park, *D. flavilinea* on the Fryingpan in Colorado, *D. grandis* on the Henry's Fork of the Snake. Green drake hatches on freestone streams with unregulated flows tend, and I write that lightly, *tend* toward being scattered to the point that trout don't feed selectively on them quite so often. But green drakes hatch on nearly every Western trout stream, and can emerge in sufficient numbers to cause selective feeding.

Green drake nymphs browse vegetation on bottom stones or feed among rooted vegetation. When ready for emergence, they swim feebly toward the top. Many emerge in the surface film, but a large proportion split the nymphal skin and the dun emerges beneath the surface. The dun then completes the trip, and it is the dun itself, not the nymph, for which I offer a soft-hackled wet fly as imitation. The dun, when finally through the surface, must sit for some time while its wet wings dry before it can fly. This is the green drake's most vulnerable stage, and the one you should concentrate on imitating. If for no other reason, the dun represents a prime dry fly opportunity. Since it might be brief, you'd be foolish to waste it.

The green drake spinner falls to the water after depositing its eggs. It lies spent until a riffle takes it under and drowns it or a trout sips it. The spinner is worth an imitation for those rare times you'll encounter trout feeding selectively on them.

Green drakes begin emerging in most places when water temperatures approach the magic 50 degree mark. That comes in late May or early June in the coastal states, through June inland, on the Henry's Fork of the Snake for example, and from late June through July in the Rocky Mountain states and provinces. A follow-up hatch of *D. coloradensis* begins in the Yellowstone region in September, at the same time as the *D. flavilinea* hatch in Colorado. There is not a month, from May through September, when a green drake hatch of one species or another is not a possibility.

One of the drawbacks of the hatch, as I've encountered it, is its unpredictability. It is fickle. Green drakes usually hatch for only a week to ten days. They might come off on any day during that period, or they might not. If the wind comes up, the hatch goes down. If the sun is too bright, the hatch might be brief or not happen at all. This lack of consistency is a major reason I prefer to spend time chasing the smaller but more constant mayfly hatches.

Daily emergence begins and ends in the hour or two surrounding noon, especially on bright days when the hatch is condensed. If the sky is cloudy the hatch might be spread from 11:00 a.m. until 3:00 or even 4:00 p.m. Most good green drake hatches, coming off in such numbers that they get the trout up and greedy for those big bodies, last between an hour and two hours. That's a relatively short time when you're in the midst of snotty trout feeding eagerly but very selectively. This is just a bit of a warning to have your ducks lined up when a green drake hatch is expected to start. Be watchful for the arrival of the big insects, and the advent of trout rising to them, so that you can get started solving the hatch and catching fish as soon as the action begins. The start of a short and hectic green drake hatch is no time to begin rebuilding your leader.

Spinner falls, when they happen in numbers sufficient to prompt selective feeding, which in my experience is not very often but important when it happens, start around the end of the daily dun emergence and go on through late afternoon and early evening. I've seen times when the spinner fall overlapped the emerging duns, so trout kept right on feeding without interruption. You need to be observant to notice that transition. If you continue to cast a dun dressing after trout have switched to spinners, you will not do well.

■ Recognition

Green drake nymphs are catagorized as crawlers. I don't believe you need to identify them much beyond that, because I believe most often they're taken opportunistically by trout and it's not necessary to imitate them specifically.

Green drake duns have three tails, which separates them from most other mayflies for which you might mistake them. The bodies of the larger species are somewhat portly, though some of the smaller species, often called the *lesser green drakes*, are slender and delicate. The duns are usually an olive-brown on the back, soft to even bright green on the underside, with distinct bands, usually of yellow, between the abdominal segments. Please note that the duns harden quickly and change colors once they're out of the water. You should capture one while it's still on the water to get a true look at what the trout are seeing.

Dun and spinner hindwings are large, and have a distinct angulation, or corner, in the leading edge. The forewings are large and slate- or lead-colored; green drake duns are sometimes called leadwing olives for the color of their wings and bodies. Their olive coloration and their large size are the key characteristics of these mayfly duns.

Green drake spinners also have three tails. Their bodies are most often a dark wine-red color on the back, a bit lighter, toward tan, on the underside. The wings are normally spent, spread on the water after the insect has laid its eggs.

WESTERN GREEN DRAKE DUN

■ Key Characteristics

Dun: Three tails.
Large hindwing with costal angulation.
Distinctly banded abdominal segments.
Size 10 to 14.
Color: Tannish to brownish olive on back, lighter olive to green on the underside.

Spinner: Three tails.
Large hindwing with costal angulation.
Size 10 to 14.
Color: Wine-red on back, lighter on underside.

WESTERN GREEN DRAKE SPINNER

■ Imitation

It's wise to carry an imitation for the subsurface dun, because it emerges from the nymphal exoskeleton beneath the water. This should be a simple soft-hackled wet for the action its fibers will offer.

Most of the imitations you carry for green drakes should be for the floating dun stage. Since this is a large insect, and generally hatches on smooth water where you need little flotation, your flies should look as much like the natural as possible. For no other insect in this book will more exact imitations be recommended. If you have the time and patience to work out the steps in tying artist Richard Bunse's Natural Dun, no other dressing will fool more trout that are feeding selectively on green drakes.

You should also carry a dressing for those uncommon times when you suddenly find that you need it to fish afternoon and evening spinner falls. The old Red Quill Spinner is the standard.

Green Drake Soft-hackle

Hook: 2X heavy, size 10 to 14.
Thread: Olive silk or 6/0 nylon.
Hackle: Olive-dyed partridge.
Rib: Single strand of yellow floss.
Body: Olive fur.

GREEN DRAKE SOFT-HACKLE

Green Paradrake (Mike Lawson)
Hook: Standard dry fly, size 12 to 14.
Thread: Yellow 3/0 Monocord.
Wings: Moose body hair, as wing post.
Tails: Three moose body hairs.
Body: Olive-dyed elk hair ribbed with working thread.

GREEN PARADRAKE

Hackle: Olive-dyed grizzly, tied parachute.

Note: Tie in the wing post first, then long tails, then tie the body hair in behind the eye of the hook. Double the hair back, rib it with thread to the end of the extended body, then back to the base of the wing post, where the hackle is tied in and wound.

NATURAL DUN

Natural Dun (Richard Bunse)

Hook: 1X short, size 12 to 14.

Thread: Yellow 6/0 nylon.

Wing: Natural dun deer hair.

Tails: Nutria or beaver guard hair fibers.

Body: Ethafoam packing foam, colored with olive waterproof pen.

Note: For lengthy and detailed instructions in tying this fly, see Skip Morris's fine book *Tying Foam Flies* (Frank Amato Publications Inc., 1994).

GREEN DRAKE DUN

Green Drake Dun (A.K. Best)

Hook: 2X long, size 12 to 14.

Thread: Olive 6/0 nylon.

Tails: Elk hip hair (substitute blue dun hackle fibers).

Body: Olive-dyed turkey biot.

Wings: Blue dun hen hackle tips.

Hackle: Blue dun, clipped on bottom.

RED QUILL SPINNER

Red Quill Spinner
Hook: Standard dry fly, size 12 to 14.
Thread: Brown 6/0 or 8/0 nylon.
Tails: Brown hackle fibers, split.
Body: Reddish brown-dyed hackle stem.
Wing: Light blue dun hen hackle tips, spent.
Hackle: Brown, clipped top and bottom.

◼ Presentation

Rig for any stage of the green drake hatch with a 10- to 14-foot leader and a long tippet of 4X or 5X. The rule on flies this size is 4X, but I often go to 5X for the softer, limper tippet to give the fly a drag-free drift on the kind of smooth water where you'll need it. Trout are often fussy about drag during the green drake hatch.

Fish the soft-hackle as an imitation for the emerging dun to rising trout during the hatch. Pinpoint the lie of a feeding trout. Cast just above and beyond it. Be sure the fly sinks, giving it a tug if necessary to get it under, then let it swing slowly across current in front of the trout. Don't set the hook hard if you feel a take. If the fish has any size, a hard hook-set will simply separate you from your fly.

Fish dry flies for both duns and spinners with the appropriate presentation for the type of water on which you're fishing. If it's smooth, which it will be most often, use cross-stream reach casts and down-stream wiggle casts, rather than an upstream presentation, to show the flies to the trout ahead of your line and leader. Richard Bunse and I once had an experience on a glassy spring creek, fishing dry flies during a great green drake hatch, when we could not fool a fish. This was a few years into our pasts, when we fished dry flies almost exclusively with upstream casts. We finally turned downstream, began using wiggle casts to drift the flies carefully into the feeding lanes of the rising trout. Those that had refused all of our flies on upstream casts suddenly became easy on any of them with downstream casts. Presentation was much more important than fly pattern, which is often true during this and many other hatches.

You'll usually have to get both pattern and presentation right to do well during a hatch of large green drakes on the smooth water they inhabit.

CHAPTER 10

GREEN DAMSELS

Order: Odonata
Family: Coenagrionidae and Lestidae

GREEN DAMSELS ARE IMPORTANT TO ANYBODY WHO fishes stillwaters. The timing of damselfly activity, in late spring and early summer, coincides with the mud-dying of many Western rivers and streams from heavy rains and snowmelt. If your favorite streams are unfishable for a few weeks, don't hang up your rods. Look instead toward local lakes and ponds. Their peak season is right around the time when stream fishing is at its worst.

Damselfly populations are found throughout the West. It's hard to imagine a lake or pond that does not have a fishable population of them. They are not restricted by altitude, latitude, or longitude. They're important in high lakes in New Mexico, Colorado, Montana, and Idaho. They're important in the lowland lakes of California, Oregon, and Washington. I've done most of my fishing over them in either Cascade Mountain lakes or windswept desert lakes. The Kamloops region in British Columbia is a hotbed for them.

The more weeds in a stillwater, the more damsels you'll find. Clear and somewhat sterile waters, some alpine lakes where weeds are sparse for example, have small populations, though you'll still find them in fishable numbers around the shallow margins. A few damselfly types live in moving water, but they are of minor importance to the angler, although they do give rise to some of the most gorgeous, vividly colored adults.

Damselflies have incomplete metamorphosis. They grow to full size in the nymph stage, emerge and mate as adults. The typical life cycle lasts one year, though some live two years as nymphs. The adults live for some weeks. Their presence is extended and they remain important long after actual emergence.

The nymphs are predaceous. They have a hinged and extensible lower labium, the equivalent of our lower jaw. When within range of prey, this shoots out, grabs the victim, and draws it in to be consumed. They stalk prey or lie in ambush along the stems and leaves of submerged vegetation. Damselfly nymphs feed on the insects and crustaceans that feed on the vegetation, which is why photosynthetic growth is so important to damsels though they are predators, and in turn why weed beds are so important to trout though they do not eat weeds.

When ready to emerge, damsel nymphs migrate from their preferred weedy habitat to the nearest emergent vegetation, which is usually at or near the shoreline. They crawl out on reed stems, logs, lily pads, or the bank itself. The nymphal skin splits down the back and the adult emerges very slowly. It is unable to fly for an hour or more. This usually takes place at dusk or after dark, a defense against bird predation. The nymph migration is the moment of most importance for damsels. They might be forced to swim one or two hundred yards or more to shore, from weed bed habitat to a shoreline emergence area. They're taken consistently and selectively by trout whenever this migration is under way.

Adults fly only in still air on sunny days. They hover around when the lake or pond is drowsing. They form a catching basket with their front legs, patrol a territory and capture mayflies, mosquitoes, and midges. Some prey are devoured in flight. When the wind comes up or the sun is hidden by a passing cloud, adult damselflies immediately go to rest, usually on vegetation extending from the water or at the shoreline. If the wind blows hard enough, they are blown from vegetation such as reed forests and lily pad flats onto the water, where trout take them.

Damselfly adults are almost always most important on sunny days when the afternoon wind comes up and also right at the edges of the lake or pond. Adults are secondary in importance to nymphs, but when trout are selective to them you need an imitation.

Damselfly nymph migrations begin in mid- to late May, continue through June on most stillwaters and go on through July on many others, especially those at higher elevations where ice-out is late. Adults hunt, mate, and lay eggs at the shoreline for several weeks, so they can be important through the entire warm part of summer.

The most important hours are in mid- to late afternoon and evening during the nymph migration. It is very difficult to notice damselfly activity beneath the surface. If you see trout taking something just subsurface, and you see just one damselfly nymph swimming laboriously toward shore, suspect that is what trout are taking and tie one on.

Adults are most important after the sun has warmed the air, which means any time from late morning through the rest of a warm day. If a wind comes up, watch for trout feeding sporadically along the edges of reeds and pads. A dry damsel pattern cast to the shore-line or to the edge of emergent vegetation and left to lie there will often draw explosions.

■ Recognition

Nymphs are easily recognized by their three tail gills, which look like willow leaves. They have long, slender bodies, wing pads held flat over the back, and the extensible labium that shoots out to grab prey. They are green to a dark olive-brown, to camouflage with the vegetation in which they live. At full growth they're an inch to an inch-and-a-half long, imitated on size 10 and 12 long-shank hooks.

Adults have long, slender bodies. Their wings are held over their backs when at rest, as opposed to dragonfly adults, which always carry their wings out to the sides when at rest. Adult damselfly colors are blue, tan, and at rare times red. Typical size is 10 or 12, again tied on long-shank hooks or with extended bodies.

GREEN DAMSEL NYMPH

■ Key Characteristics

Nymph: Three willow-leaf tail gills.
Slender body.
Extensible lower labium.
Size 10 to 12.
Color: Green to olive-brown.

Adult: Long, slender abdomen.
Wings held together over back when at rest.
Eyes bead-like and separated.
Size 10 to 12.
Color: Blue, tan, or red.

DAMSELFLY ADULT

■ Imitation

Fly patterns for damselfly nymphs should incorporate some sort of pliable material that works well in the water, to represent the snakelike swimming of the natural. This internal action is important because you'll often fish the flies with a slow retrieve, or no retrieve at all, and the fly itself must still have some sort of movement. Marabou is best for the way it moves when wet.

Patterns for adults should be as imitative as possible. Flotation is not the problem it is on riffles and runs. Your fly should show an excellent silhouette of a natural damselfly trapped in the surface of a stillwater.

GREEN DAMSEL

Green Damsel (Polly Rosborough)
Hook: 2X or 3X long, size 10 to 12.
Thread: Olive 3/0 Monocord or 6/0 nylon.
Tails: Pale olive marabou, pinched short.
Body: Pale olive rabbit fur noodle.
Legs: Olive-dyed teal flank fibers.
Wing pads: Olive marabou, one shade darker than tail.
Note: Roll the fur into a noodle in the palm of your hand. Twist it with a thread loop, forming a tight fur rope. When wound on the hook this will form a segmented body. Pick out the fur in honor of the author of *Tying and Fishing the Fuzzy Nymphs* (Stackpole Books, 1988).

HOFFMAN GREEN DAMSEL

Hoffman Green Damsel (Henry Hoffman)
Hook: 3X long, size 10 to 12, bent slightly upward.
Thread: Olive 6/0 or 8/0 nylon.
Eyes: 50# monofilament burned to knobs.
Tail: Olive Chickabou fluff.

Rib: Fine gold wire.

Body: Olive Chickabou fibers as herl.

Legs: Chickabou fiber tips.

Head: Olive Antron dubbing between eyes.

Note: This excellent dressing by Henry Hoffman, of Super Grizzly hackle fame, has taken so many trout for me that I highly recommend you purchase the Chickabou patches Henry is marketing and learn to tie the fly.

OLIVE WOOLLY BUGGER

Olive Woolly Bugger

Hook: 3X long, size 10 to 12.

Weight: 10 to 20 turns of lead wire.

Thread: Olive 6/0 nylon.

Tail: Olive marabou, thinned out.

Body: Olive chenille.

Hackle: Brown hen, clipped from rear half of fly, and from the top and bottom.

Note: Take a standard Olive Woolly Bugger, which you should always have in your fly boxes, thin out the tails by half, then cut or pinch off all of the hackle except a few fibers sticking out to each side for legs. This makes an excellent damselfly nymph imitation.

PARACHUTE DAMSEL

Parachute Damsel

Hook: 2X or 3X long, size 10 to 12.

Thread: Black 6/0 nylon.

Parachute post: Blue, tan, or red bucktail.

Body: Blue, tan, or red bucktail, extended, ribbed with working thread.

Hackle: Light blue dun, parachute.

Head: Butts of wing post fibers pulled forward, tied off, and clipped short.

ADULT DAMSEL

Adult Damsel (Andy Burk)
Hook: Standard dry fly, size 10.
Thread: Blue or coffee 3/0.
Abdomen: Blue or light brown Z-lon or Damsel Body, extended.
Wings: Light blue dun hackle tips.
Body: Blue or tan deer hair, spun and clipped.
Legs: Blue or coffee 3/0 thread, three strands.
Eyes: Monofilament nymph eyes.
Note: To form the Z-lon body, select a skein of Z-lon, hold the ends in the thumb and forefinger of each hand, twist it tightly, then bring your fingertips toward each other. The Z-lon, under tension, will magically twist itself into the extended body you're after.

■ Presentation

For nymphing, rig with either a floating or wet-tip line. I usually use a floater because the nymphs usually migrate fairly near to the top. I suspect I'm missing many opportunities when the nymphs migrate deeper and I do not even notice them. With a floating line the leader should be around 10 to 12 feet long. With a wet-tip keep the leader to around 7 1/2 to 8 feet.

Cast long and let the fly sink for some time. Watch your line tip for signs of a take as the fly sinks. Retrieve with a combination of a slow hand-twist then a somewhat fast stripping retrieve, interspersed with pauses to simply let the fly settle. Some days trout take on the hand-twist, some days on the strip. I get most of my takes, on all days, when the fly is on the drop.

I've heard that the nymph is most effective when cast away from shore and retrieved toward it, because the naturals migrate toward shore for emergence and that is the only direction trout see them swimming. I can't say from my own experience that this is critical. However, I recommend you keep it in mind when fishing damselfly nymph imitations.

When fishing adult dressings, confine most of your casting to the shoreline and reed or lily pad edges. Present the fly all along the edge, as you might a bass bug. If a dead sit doesn't draw any strikes, try twitching the fly as if it were a natural damsel adult struggling against its distasteful position on the water.

CHAPTER 11

ANTS

Order: Formicidae

CARPENTER ANTS LIVE IN ALL WESTERN FORESTS, AND have dispersal flights in spring and early summer. They are winged, though for only one flight. They leave the old nest, fly wherever the winds and their fragile wings take them. If that feeble flight takes them over a stream or lake, when they tumble down they become fare for trout.

Wingless ants are smaller. They are more common in drier habitats than carpenter ants. It's tempting to say one form is important in forests, the other in deserts, but that's not true. Wingless ants live everywhere, and can be important wherever grass and shrubs overhang water that is fishable.

You will find few trout waters in the entire West that are not visited at times by ants in fishable numbers. Carpenter ants are more important on small streams and lakes than they are on large rivers and big lakes because the smaller the body of water, the more of it lies in close proximity to the trees from which the ants take wing.

Wingless ants are most important in streams that have constant and stable flows through grass and shrub country. Spring creeks and tailwaters do not work their banks back to gravel bars, as spate streams usually do, tending instead to erode steadily and deeply right at the edges. Wherever trout hold tight to such banks, they are likely to see ants as part of their diet at times.

Wingless ants are usually tiny. They will be a factor in selective feeding only when the water is calm enough that they float in the surface film. Their importance is restricted to smooth flows very near the banks.

Dispersal flights of carpenter ants take place in the first warm days of spring and early summer. They will be spread over May and June in the various regions of the West, but normally last only a week or two on any one body of water. The daily flight begins when the air warms up, usually around ten in the morning or a little later. Winged ants will continue to fly all day. Those that land on logs and rocks in lakes and streams will lose their wings and continue running around until they find a place to begin a new colony, or fall to the water and get taken by trout.

Wingless ants begin their terrestrial marches when the heat of late spring or summer reaches into the earth and warms their colonies. They can be important any time from June through late September, when cool nights cause them to retreat into their nests. Daily importance is any time the day is warm. They get restless and start out around nine or ten in the morning, and continue getting into trouble with trout along the edges right into the evening if the day is warm enough.

■ Recognition

The wasp-waisted ant shape is a key to identification. They have the distinct big gaster at the after end, the fairly large bulb of a head, and the slender thorax between. Carpenter ants have wings but lose them quickly after landing. One key to their presence is a scattering of discarded wings on rocks and logs at streamside or lakeshore. If you see lots of these wings, even without seeing any ants, you can assume their presence and take trout with an imitation.

■ Key Characteristics

JIM SCHOLLMEYER

Distinct gaster and head.
Slender thorax.
Wings on carpenter ants.
Carpenter ants size 10 to 14.
Wingless ants size 16 to 22 or smaller.
Color: Black or cinammon brown.

ANT

FLYING ANT

JIM SCHOLLMEYER

■ Imitation

Carpenter ants are winged, and also somewhat dense in relation to their size. If they touch down on water they sink quickly. Most, I suspect, are taken by trout when they are submerged rather than on the surface. If you have little luck with a floating dressing, rub it with mud or wet it with saliva and fish it wet. You'll be surprised how often trout suddenly accept it. Fishing a floating black fly in the dark surroundings of a forest is not the easiest thing to do, anyway. The fly is difficult to see on the water. Fish it sunk, on the swing, and you can feel takes as tugs or thumps.

Wingless ants float flush in the surface film. Your imitations should be sparsely hackled, with the bottom clipped so the body is lowered right into the film. You'll be fishing them on smooth water anyway, where form rather than flotation is the critical aspect of the fly.

With all ants, the most important thing in tying is the distinct separation of the back bulb from the front bulb. Do not let the body segments blend into each other.

Black Fur Ant
Hook: Standard dry fly, size 16 to 22.
Thread: Black 6/0 or 8/0 nylon.
Gaster: Black fur or synthetic dubbing.
Hackle: Black, sparse, clipped on bottom.
Head: Black fur or synthetic dubbing.

BLACK FUR ANT

CINNAMON FUR ANT

Cinnamon Fur Ant
Hook: Standard dry fly, size 16 to 22.
Thread: Brown 6/0 or 8/0 nylon.
Gaster: Cinnamon brown fur or synthetic dubbing.
Hackle: Brown, sparse, clipped on bottom.
Head: Cinnamon brown fur or synthetic dubbing.

Winged Black Ant
Hook: Standard dry fly, size 10 to 14.

WINGED BLACK ANT

Thread: Black 6/0 or 8/0 nylon.
Gaster: Black fur or synthetic dubbing.
Hackle: Black, sparse.
Wings: Grizzly hackle tips.
Head: Black fur or synthetic dubbing.

Foam Quick-Sight Ant
Hook: Standard dry fly, size 12 to 20.
Thread: Black 6/0 or 8/0 nylon.
Body: Quick-Sight body or black foam painted white on tip.
Hackle: Black, clipped on bottom.
Note: You can buy Orvis Quick-Sight bodies, or cut your own out of black foam and paint one tip white. They're neater if you buy them, cheaper if you make your own.

FOAM QUICK-SIGHT ANT

Foam Ant
(Skip Morris)
Hook: Standard dry fly, size 14 to 22.
Thread: Black or brown 6/0 or 8/0 nylon.
Body: Black or red-brown closed-cell foam.
Indicator: Yellow yarn.
Hackle: Black or brown, undersized.
Head: Black or red-brown closed-cell foam.

FOAM ANT

■ Presentation

When you fish carpenter ant imitations on streams, the water will usually be small and freestone, at least relatively rough. Give the Winged Ant a try as a floater

in glides and pools. Rig with a 9- to 10-foot leader, 4X or 5X tippet. If trout take the fly on the surface, and you can see it happen, all is well in the world. If trout refuse it, try keeping the rigging precisely the same, but turn and fish the fly downstream on a slow swing as a wet. That will often coax trout that refuse the fly when it is a dry.

When fishing carpenter ants on lakes and ponds, rig with a 10- to 12-foot leader in 5X or 6X. Try the flies floating near the shoreline and around protruding boulders or floating logs, especially if you see trout rising in those areas. If trout refuse the fly on the float, wet it and fish it to the same areas, even to rises, on the sink or with a slow hand-twist retrieve.

You'll almost always fish the smaller wingless ant imitations on spring creeks, tailwaters, or very near freestone stream banks where grasses and low shrubs overhang smooth water. This is the most critical presentation fishing. Rig for it with a light floating line, 5-weight at the heaviest down to a 3-weight or even 2-weight. The leader should be long, 12 to 14 feet, and fine, with a two- or three-foot tippet of 5X or 6X, possibly even 7X with the tiniest ant patterns.

Cast precisely into the feeding lane of a sipping and selective trout. If you must move into position to fish upstream to the trout, cast so close to its nose that only the tippet crosses above it in the air. If possible, move into position to fish with a cross-stream reach cast or downstream wiggle cast. That way the trout sees nothing but the tiny fly arriving to it as if unattached. The closer you can fish these tiny patterns, and the shorter your casts, the more likely you'll entertain some trout.

CHAPTER 12

PALE MORNING DUNS

Order: Ephemeroptera
Family: Ephemerellidae
Genus: *Ephemerella*
Species: *inermis, infrequens*

I RANK THE PALE MORNING DUNS EQUAL, OR SOMETIMES second, to the little olives, *Baetis*, but consider both more important than the Western green drakes. All three hatch groups contain more than a single species, and will cause selective feeding by trout in nearly every Western stream at one time or another throughout the season. A fly box that lacked imitations for any of the three of these important mayfly hatches could not be said to be complete.

Pale morning duns hatch in the San Juan River in New Mexico, Hat Creek in California, the Deschutes and Metolius in Oregon, the Yakima in Washington, and are famous for their abundance in the Henry's Fork and South Fork of the Snake River in Idaho. All of Montana's major rivers have PMD hatches. The Green in Wyoming and Utah has great hatches, as does the Fryingpan and many other Colorado rivers. Alberta's famous Bow River is perhaps the best example of pale morning dun water, with stable summer flows and lots of rooted vegetation.

PMDs are most heavily distributed in spring creeks and tailwaters, with their stabilized flows. But PMD hatches are also excellent in freestone streams, coming off in many of them in greater numbers than the more sporadic green drakes and the consistent little olives. Pale morning duns are most abundant in streams with stabilized flows and rooted vegetation.

Pale morning duns have incomplete metamorphosis, spending most of a single year in the nymph stage. Although many nymphs are taken by trout, it's doubtful that they're often taken selectively. Searching dressings such as the Gold Ribbed Hare's Ear will do fine for them, though you must remember that a mature natural PMD nymph is size 16. It's critical that you use size 16 and 18 nymphs, not size 10 and 12, when fishing searching nymphs in waters where little olives and pale morning duns are the main mayfly populations.

When ready to emerge, the PMD nymph swims feebly toward the top. In many individuals the nymphal skin splits just beneath the surface and the dun emerges there, a few inches deep, to complete the trip to the surface film. It takes some time for the wings to dry before the insect can fly. Since this all happens out in open water the entire process attracts feeding trout.

Spinner falls take place in the afternoon just after the hatch, or in the evening. I've not encountered them very often in numbers that prompt trout to become selective to them. I suspect you'll rarely find need for an imitation of a spinner of the pale morning dun. If you do, you'll be glad to have it aboard.

Pale morning dun hatches begin in late May and early June in the Pacific coastal states. They are frequent in June and July inland and slightly higher. In some Rocky Mountain waters they come off as late as September and early October. The hatch on most rivers and streams goes on daily for weeks, sometimes even a couple of months. The long emergence period is a large part of PMD importance.

Daily emergence can begin as early as 9:00 in the morning on warm days. An 11:00 a.m. start is more common. On bright days the hatch might be compacted into an hour or so. On cloudy days it might start at 10:00 or 11:00 and go on until 3:00 or 4:00 in the afternoon. Such long hatches will usually not be dense, but will nearly always show enough duns to the trout to get them up and feeding selectively on the surface. The best fishing, in my experience, occurs when the pale morning dun hatch is spread and somewhat sporadic rather than short and massed. You can take your fishing at a leisurely pace when the hatch lasts three or four hours.

■ Recognition

Pale morning duns are characterized by three tails in the dun and spinner stages. The duns have pale yellowish forewings and hindwings, similar in color to the body. The body is pale yellow on the back in the female, but a mix of pale yellow and pale olive on the underside, which is what trout see. Pale morning duns often display sexual dimorphism: males and females are different colors. The males are usually pale amber on the body and wings, with large amber eyes. I've noticed that at times you see all males on the water, at other times all females, but I have not encountered this often enough to sort it out consistently.

The bodies of most pale morning duns are a mix of yellow and olive on the undersides. The dominance in the mix varies from stream to stream. I usually use the same 50/50 mix of pale yellow and light olive fur for all of my pale morning dun imitations. But you should carefully observe the insects that emerge on your own waters. If trout are critical about color, you will do far better if you get the mix just right for the water you're on most often.

PALE MORNING DUN

◼ Key Characteristics

Dun: Three tails.

Sharp costal angulation of hindwing.

Sexual dimorphism in some:

Males pale amber.

Females pale yellow/olive.

Size 16 to 20.

◼ Imitation

I recommend that you carry a soft-hackle dressing, originated by Fred Arbona and recorded in his masterful *Mayflies, the Angler, and the Trout* (Winchester Press, 1980), to match the emerging duns beneath the water. Options for matching the duns, the most important stage in my experience, include the Sparkle Dun as a dun with the trailing nymphal shuck still attached, the Hairwing Dun as a fully formed dun, and the Burned-wing Dun, all for the smooth flows where these insects hatch most often. One spinner dressing will round-out the list for those rare moments when you find the spinners important.

Emerging Pale Morning Dun

(Fred Arbona, Jr.)

EMERGING PALE MORNING DUN

Hook: Standard dry fly, size 14 to 18.

Thread: Light olive 6/0 or 8/0 nylon.

Body: Pale yellow dubbing ribbed with working thread.

Underhackle: Four turns light dun hen.

Overhackle: Two turns light ginger.

Pale Morning Sparkle Dun (Craig Mathews)

Hook: Standard dry fly, size 16 to 20.
Thread: Pale yellow 6/0 or 8/0 nylon.
Wing: Bleached coastal deer hair, in 160 degree arc over body.
Tail: Amber Antron yarn.
Body: 50/50 mix of pale yellow and light olive fur.

PALE MORNING SPARKLE DUN

Pale Morning Hairwing Dun (René Harrop)

Hook: Standard dry fly, size 16 to 20.
Thread: Pale yellow 6/0 or 8/0 nylon.
Tails: Ginger hackle fibers, split.
Body: 50/50 mix of pale yellow and light olive fur.
Hackle: Light ginger, five turns over thorax, clipped on bottom.
Wing: Bleached calf elk or coastal deer hair.
Head: Wing butts clipped Elk Hair Caddis style.

PALE MORNING
HAIRWING DUN

Burned-wing Dun

Hook: Standard dry fly, size 16 to 20.
Thread: Pale yellow 6/0 or 8/0 nylon.

BURNED-WING DUN

Wings: Light ginger hen, burned or cut to shape.
Tails: Ginger hackle fibers, split.
Body: Hackle stem dyed pale yellow/olive.
Hackle: Light ginger, parachute.

Pale Morning Quill Spinner

Hook: Standard dry
fly, size 16 to 20.
Thread: Pale yellow
6/0 or 8/0 nylon.
Tails: Light ginger
hackle fibers.
Body: Hackle stem
dyed amber.
Wings: Light ginger
hackle tips.
Hackle: Light
ginger.

PALE MORNING
QUILL SPINNER

■ Presentation

When fishing the
soft-hackle as an
emerger, try to work to a single rising fish. Cast just
above and beyond it, be sure the fly gets through the
surface film so it doesn't cut a wake, then let it swing
slowly in front of the trout's position. If a pod of trout
are rising, you can swing it through the herd of them.
If no trout are rising, it might make a good searching
pattern in the time preceding a hatch, though a size 16
Gold Ribbed Hare's Ear nymph fished on the bottom
would likely be better.

PMD dry flies will usually be fished over smooth
water to selective trout that have been cast over often.
Rig with your lightest floating line, on your presentation outfit. Use a long leader and tippet that is 2 to 3
feet long, 5X or 6X. 7X will help you hook fish, but will
not let you land many of the kind that feed on a heavy
pale morning dun hatch.

If the shape of the water allows it, always position
yourself to cast with a cross-stream reach cast or
downstream wiggle cast. Execute your most delicate
delivery. If the PMD hatch happens on a freestone
stream that is somewhat rough, then fishing upstream
will present no problems. But that will not be common
during the pale morning dun hatch. You usually need
to fish as fine and with as much finesse as you can
accomplish.

CHAPTER 13

GRAY DRAKES

Order: Ephemeroptera
Family: Baetidae
Genus: *Siphlonurus*
Species: *occidentalis*

THE GRAY DRAKE MAYFLY HAS SCATTERED IMPORTANCE. In a few places in the West it has massive hatches. The Williamson River in southern Oregon is one of them. A few Northern California streams have good populations. Silver Creek in Idaho has the hatch. Not many other waters do. When it is encountered, however, it is necessary to be armed with flies that match it.

Gray drake nymphs are found only in low-gradient streams with slow flows. Such streams, by their nature, meander among grass and reed edges, have silty deposits on the bottom, and offer lots of undercut banks. Waters inhabited by gray drakes are almost always big-fish streams.

Gray drake nymphs are swimmer mayflies, with the torpedo-shaped bodies of that type. They travel in schools, especially around their time for emergence, darting across the silty bottom or among the weed beds of their typical slow-stream habitat. They gather at the edges in and near emergent vegetation such as reeds and submerged grasses. I've swished a collecting net through a shallow bay of grass on the Williamson River in the high water of June, and had it come up from a single sweep wriggling with enough gray drake nymphs to feed a trout for a week. Trout follow these masses and feed on them at the edges.

Gray drake nymphs crawl out on protruding vegetation to emerge. Like most insects with such behavior, they do it at dusk or after dark to prevent bird predation. The duns, on account of this, have little importance except on a few cloudy afternoons when they emerge early and the wind blows enough of them onto the water to cause trout to feed selectively.

Spinner falls happen mid- to late afternoon, and can be incredible. I've seen times on the Williamson River when it was nearly necessary to wear a face mask to keep from ingesting them. When they fall in such numbers, trout feed greedily on them. The spinner is the most important stage of the gray drake hatch, though you'll also do well fishing a nymph prior to the spinner fall.

Seasonal emergence of gray drakes comes in late spring, and is often timed with high water from snowmelt or runoff from rains. It's likely nature has worked it out this way so the nymphs have places to crawl out where water has inundated streamside vegetation. This happens early to late June in most coastal states, into mid-July inland and in the Rockies.

Daily emergence occurs at dusk or after dark except on blustery days. The emergence itself is of minor importance. Fishing nymphs tight to the grass and reed edges in the hours before dark can be very productive. Spinner falls begin in the afternoon, and sometimes go on into the early evening. They're the most important part of the hatch.

■ Recognition

Nymphs of the gray drake are streamlined. They have three tails heavily fringed with hairs. The gills are large, as you would expect of an insect living in slow, poorly oxygenated flows. The key feature that separates gray drake nymphs from the speckle-wing quills,

GRAY DRAKE NYMPH

GRAY DRAKE SPINNER

Callibaetis, are the short antennae of the gray drake nymphs.

Gray drake duns, which I'll not list since they're not so important, have two tails, light gray wings, and a body that is dark gray on the backside but light gray underneath where trout see it.

Spinners, the most important stage, have two tails, clear wings, and wine-colored bodies. The underside of the spinner is lighter and tends more to gray than to the red of the back.

■ Key Characteristics

Nymph: Swimmer mayfly shape.

Three fringed tails of equal length.

Large gills, doubled on abdominal segments 1 to 2 or 1 to 7.

Antennae shorter than 2-1/2 times width of head.

Size 10 to 12.

Color: Gray to tannish gray.

Spinner: Two tails.

Wings clear, glassy.

Hindwing large.

Size 12 to 14.

Color: Body wine-red to almost black on back, lighter on underside.

■ Imitation

You should carry one or two nymph patterns if you have a chance to run into this insect. Even if trout are not feeding selectively on them, wherever the population is present they'll likely accept an imitation of the nymph because they'll be seeing them as part of their diet consistently. The Grey Wulff is considered the standard dun dressing, but in truth a size 12 Adams will do just as well for you, and it's likely you already carry that fly as a searching dressing.

Spinners are the most important but least solved stage of the hatch. Polly Rosborough's Black Drake Spinner is tied for the *S. occidentalis* hatch. I believe it captures the color of the back of the insect, but not the belly that the trout see. I recommend that you try it, and try the listed Gray Quill Spinner, but compare the naturals you collect to the color of your dyed quill when it is wet, to be sure you've got it right. I don't run into the hatch often enough on my waters to have followed this comparison to a conclusion.

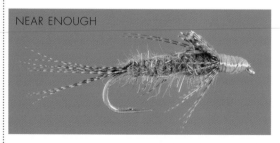

NEAR ENOUGH

Near Enough (Polly Rosborough)
Hook: 2X or 3X long, size 10 to 12.

Thread: Gray 3/0 Monocord.
Tails: Mallard flank.
Body: Gray fox fur, as noodle.
Wing pads: Mallard flank fibers, trimmed.
Legs: Tips of wing pad fibers.

BLACK DRAKE NYMPH

Black Drake Nymph (Polly Rosborough)
Hook: 2X or 3X long, size 10 to 12.
Thread: Gray 3/0 Monocord.
Tails: Speckled guinea fibers.
Body: Muskrat fur noodle.
Wing pads: Grayish black ostrich herl flues.
Legs: Speckled guinea fibers.

BLACK DRAKE SPINNER

Black Drake Spinner (Polly Rosborough)
Hook: 1X long, size 10 to 12.
Thread: Dark gray 3/0 Monocord or 6/0 nylon.
Tails: Rusty purplish gray hackle fibers.*
Rib: Working thread.
Body: Blend of purple and brown fur or synthetic.
Wings: Rusty purplish gray hackle tips.*
Hackle: Rusty purplish gray.*
*Polly calls for a special dye bath to achieve the proper color for the hackle, wings, and tails. You can substitute a dark blue dun.

Gray Quill Spinner
Hook: Standard dry fly, size 10 to 14.
Thread: Gray 6/0 or 8/0 nylon.

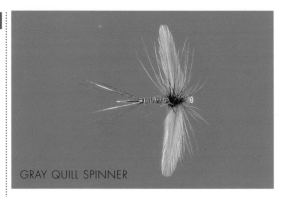

GRAY QUILL SPINNER

Tail: Blue dun hackle fibers, split.
Body: Gray-dyed hackle stem.
Wings: Light blue dun hen hackle tips, spent.
Hackle: Blue dun, clipped top and bottom.

■ Presentation

Rig for the nymph with a floating line and a leader around ten feet long, with a fairly stout 3X or 4X tippet or with a wet-tip line and shorter leader, six feet or so. The wet-tip line delivers the fly deeper. Fish nymphs along grass edges and especially undercut banks. On the silty and deep-cut meadow streams populated most often by gray drakes, this usually means either fishing from the near bank and letting the fly swing in toward you, or fishing from the far bank and letting the fly drift down along an undercut as far as possible before the current draws it away.

You'll need to rig finer for the spinners, down to a long tippet of 4X or 5X. You'll rarely fish these flies over anything but smooth currents. Your position, because of the nature of the streams, will usually be kneeling on the bank. It's critical to fish the cross-stream reach cast or downstream wiggle cast to rising fish, rather than casting upstream to them and lining them.

The trout you see feeding on gray drakes will often be large, and will always be quite selective during these spinner falls. Of course, you can always follow the great Polly's advice and ignore the spinners, swinging a nymph under the rises to interest the largest trout that refuse to come up for surface fare.

CHAPTER 14

GRAY SEDGES

Order: Trichoptera
Family: Rhyacophilidae
Genus: *Rhyacophila*
Species: 57 in Western states

GRAY SEDGE ADULTS ARE CALLED GREEN ROCK WORMS in the larval stage. With nearly 60 species distributed throughout the entire West, they are as important as any aquatic insect in terms of numbers eaten by trout. Caddis suffer slightly by comparison with mayflies when you consider that mayfly hatches tend to be condensed, happen during daylight, and emerge out in open water where trout are suddenly treated to an overabundance of them right where you can see it happening and match it. Caddis, including gray sedges, tend to spread out their emergence period, or hide it at dusk and after dark, causing less selective and also less visible feeding by trout. That puts the burden on the angler to recognize when these insects are important, because trout do feed on them heavily, and nearly everywhere, in the West.

The green rock worm larvae that give rise to the gray sedge adults are fast-water insects, most abundant in streams with rocky beds and well-oxygenated currents. Their heaviest populations are in freestone streams with steep gradients and lots of pebbles and cobble on the bottom. That usually means mountain streams and rivers with lots of riffles and runs: most folks' favorite kind of water.

They are present in fishable numbers in almost any trout stream in the Cascade, Sierra, and Rocky Mountain chains, and the foothills where these waters gentle out. They are less prevalent in meandering valley rivers, though they'll be found there, too, wherever the water tumbles over a rocky riffle.

Gray sedges, like all caddisflies, have complete metamorphosis, with larval, pupal, and adult stages. The larvae are predaceous. They prowl among niches between stones in riffles and runs, hunting for mayfly, midge, and blackfly larvae. This restless activity, in such rough water, causes them to be knocked loose often. Trout see them adrift in abundance wherever populations are significant. Though the larvae might not prompt selective feeding, they are taken often enough that a green rock worm imitation, properly presented along the bottom, will rarely be allowed to drift unmolested by trout.

Pupation takes place on the bottom, in a crude shelter constructed for the purpose. When mature, the pupa cuts free and either drifts downstream along the bottom for some way, or immediately begins its ascent to the surface. The swim to the top is aided by gases trapped under the pupal skin, and can be quite swift. The insect is very vulnerable to trout during this trip. It's quite likely that more gray sedges are taken as pupae on the ascent than as adults on the surface.

As soon as the pupa reaches the surface, the adult splits free of the pupal skin. The adult wings remain dry inside the pupal shuck, so the adult is able to fly without delay. It leaves the surface at once, takes off and heads for streamside vegetation in a hurry. Trout are able to capture the rising pupae much more easily than the escaping adults, which is one reason feeding during a hatch appears to be on adults, but is more likely to be concentrated on pupae just before they reach the surface. Keep this in mind when you see trout rising in fast water and see gray sedges in the air but fail to catch many trout with dry flies. Switch to a pupal pattern and you're likely to start catching trout.

Gray sedge adults live up to three weeks. They mate in the vegetation and return sporadically to lay their eggs over the same riffles and runs from which they arose earlier. Gray sedge females usually dive into the water and swim down to lay their eggs on bottom stones. This is a key bit of behavior. Again, if you see adults in the air, and observe sporadic splashy rises, trout might be taking more winged adults beneath the surface than on top. Try a wet fly and you might suddenly start catching trout.

With so many Western species, gray sedge hatches are spread over several summer months. They begin as early as May in the coastal states and provinces and extend into early October. Warm days of June and July see the heaviest hatches on the mountain streams where populations are greatest. I think of gray sedges as insects of sunshine. Adults will be out and dancing over boisterous riffles and runs during the middle of the day when the sun is high and the air is warm, in the heat of midsummer. Gray sedges and other caddis hatches rise in importance as mayfly hatches tend to dwindle after their spring and early summer dominance.

The gray sedge hatch itself is difficult to pin down. It often happens at dusk or after dark. But it also can be spread out over several midday hours. Ovipositing flights often happen during the brightest part of the day. You'll see those splashy rises, see a sprinkling of adults in the air. You'll almost always enjoy some success fishing a dry fly. But consider that trout might be feeding subsurface on pupae ascending to hatch, or on adults descending to lay their eggs.

Fish larval patterns in riffles and runs any time your collecting reveals fair populations of green rock worms on bottom stones. Fish pupal patterns whenever you see adults in the air and fish rising, but cannot catch them on dry flies. It's also wise to suspend a pupal dressing beneath the dry fly when you're catching a few on the surface, but think you should be doing better. Fish dry flies whenever you see adults in the air and trout rising. This will usually be during the bright part of the day or just at dusk. You'll often enjoy excellent success with the dry fly. If you do not do well on dries, try swinging a pupal pattern or a traditional winged wet fly across the current. That will often solve the problem.

■ Recognition

Green rock worms are among the easiest of aquatic insects to recognize. They are fleshy and worm-like, have claws called *anal hooks* in place of their tails, and have a single hardened plate behind the head. This separates them from the larvae of spotted sedges, which are similar but have three hardended plates behind the head.

It's difficult to give a firm fix on the pupal stage of any caddis, because their features are transitional between the larvae and adults. Even entomologists identify pupae by rearing them and associating them with the larvae from which they arise or the adults into which they turn. In general, gray sedge pupae are olive, size 12 to 16, and abundant where you find lots of green rock worm larvae and gray sedge adults.

Gray sedge adults have gray wings that are usually spotted or mottled. Their bodies are dark tan to green, at times so dark they're almost black. Adult antennae are slightly shorter than the body.

GRAY SEDGE LARVA

GRAY SEDGE PUPA

▌ Key Characteristics

Larvae: Pair of anal hooks on last segment.
Fleshy abdomen and thorax with spike gills.
Single hardened plate on first thoracic
segment.
Heavy mandibles.
Size 10 to 16.
Color: Dark to bright green.
Pupae: Size 12 to 16.
Color: Generally olive.
Adults: No tails.
Gray wings, often mottled or with spots.
Antennae shorter than body.
Size 12 to 16.
Color: Body dark tan or green.

GRAY SEDGE ADULT

JIM SCHOLLMEYER

▌ Imitation

You'll be wise to carry imitations of each of the three
stages of this insect: larva, pupa, and adult. In addition
to the dry for the adult, a standard winged wet, the
Leadwing Coachman, will take a surprising number of
trout during an egg-laying flight, and you should add it
to your list of flies to match this hatch.

GREEN CADDIS LARVA

Green Caddis Larva
Hook: Curved scud or bait hook, size 10 to 16.

Weight: 10 to 20 turns lead wire, diameter of hook shank.
Thread: Brown 6/0 or 8/0 nylon.
Abdomen: Olive to bright green fur or synthetic dubbing.
Legs: Gray partridge fibers.
Thorax: Brown fur dubbing, picked out.

Partridge & Green
(Sylvester Nemes)
Hook: 2X heavy, size 12 to 16.
Thread: Green Gossamer silk or 6/0 nylon.
Hackle: Gray partridge.
Body: Silk working thread or green silk floss.
Thorax: Hare's mask fur.

PARTRIDGE & GREEN

Brown and Bright Green Deep Sparkle Pupa (Gary LaFontaine)
Hook: Standard dry fly, size 12 to 16.
Weight: 10 to 15 turns lead wire diameter of the hook shank or one size finer.
Thread: Brown 6/0 or 8/0 nylon.
Overbody: Medium olive Antron yarn, teased out top and bottom, brought forward.
Underbody: 1/2 olive Antron yarn, 1/2 olive fur, mixed.
Legs and antennae: Dark grouse fibers.
Head: Hare's mask fur.

BROWN AND BRIGHT GREEN DEEP SPARKLE PUPA

Deer Hair Caddis (Jim Schollmeyer)
Hook: Standard dry fly, size 12 to 16.
Thread: Olive 6/0 or 8/0 nylon.
Hackle: Dark blue dun, palmered over body.
Body: Dark olive fur or synthetic dubbing.
Wing: Natural dun deer hair.

OLIVE X-CADDIS

Olive X-Caddis (John Juracek and Craig
   Mathews)
Hook: Standard dry fly, size 12 to 16.
Thread: Olive 8/0 nylon.
Tail: Amber Z-lon.
Body: Olive Antron dubbing.
Wing: Natural dun deer hair.
Head: Butts of wing hair.

Leadwing Coachman
Hook: 2X heavy, size 12 to 14.
Thread: Black 6/0 or 8/0 nylon.
Body: Peacock herl.
Hackle: Brown or furnace hen.
Wing: Goose or dark mallard primary quill sections.

LEADWING COACHMAN

■ Presentation

Rig for nymphing with a shot and indicator setup. Use a floating line and attach an 8- to 10-foot leader, tapered to 4X or 5X. Locate the indicator two to three times the depth of the water up the leader. Use enough shot to get the fly to the bottom and keep it there. Cast upstream in fairly fast and rough water. Mend and tend the line so that the indicator floats downstream just as a dry fly might. That is your best indication the nymph is drifting freely near the bottom. If you get no hits, rig to fish deeper. Cover all of the likely lies in a riffle or brisk run.

Fish pupal and adult patterns on a 10- to 12-foot leader, tapered to 4X or 5X. Cast across and downstream with the subsurface flies, and mend the line constantly to slow the drift of the fly in the fast water where this method is most effective. Or you might prefer suspending one of the wet flies beneath your dry on a 20-inch tippet. That can work wonders. If you haven't tried a dropper, tied directly to the hook bend of the dry fly, it's a method that you should give a trial next time out.

The upstream dry fly presentation will work well on the kind of rough water where gray sedge adults hang out. You'll rarely need to worry about the fine-tuned rigging and delicate casts required on smooth water. You will want to fish as close to your dry fly as possible, with short casts: it's difficult to follow the drift of such a drab fly on rough water if your cast is much longer than forty feet.

CHAPTER 15

SPOTTED SEDGES

Order: Trichoptera
Family: Hydropsychidae
Genus: *Hydropsyche*
Species: 25 Western

SPOTTED SEDGE ADULTS ARISE FROM NET-SPINNING caddis larvae, which are similar in appearance to green rock worms. Gary LaFontaine, author of *Caddisflies* (Lyons & Burford, 1981) calls the spotted sedge the single most important trout-stream insect. I agree in terms of trout foods, and general activity on trout streams, though I also believe that little olive and pale morning dun mayflies cause more selective feeding situations. But numerous days on Western trout streams are made more productive and pleasant each season by the abundant presence of spotted sedges.

Spotted sedge larvae are net-spinnners, and therefore filter feeders. They spin a tiny net in the current and feed on whatever collects in it. Their populations explode wherever the hand of man intrudes on the natural balance of a stream by adding particulate matter that can be captured in their nets. So many streams in the West have been dammed or diverted through irrigation systems that this caddis group has grown enormously in importance. They are abundant in every state and province. In a few waters, such as the Bighorn River in Montana, they come off in numbers so great that you're often forced to cover your ears to keep them from crawling in.

These net-spinning larvae inhabit only moving water, and need rocky bottoms for the best deployment of their nets. You'll find them in cascades and riffles of swift mountain streams, and in the long, slow runs of the largest tailwater rivers. They seem especially important on large and famous rivers, though it's difficult to say whether the caddis become famous for their presence in these rivers or the rivers become famous for the presence of these prolific caddis.

Spotted sedges have complete metamorphosis, with larval, pupal, and adult stages. Each stage is important to the angler.

The larvae live on the bottom, where they crawl among stones until they find suitable locations to build crude retreats. They spin small silken nets between rocks, distended directly in the current. In the natural scheme of things, these nets capture bits of leaves, twigs, and other vegetation. When man runs water through fields for irrigation and returns it to a stream, it carries lots of particulate matter such as cow manure. This enriches the stream for filter-feeding caddis.

Plankton does not grow in moving water. When man builds a dam on a river, plankton grows in the reservoir. The plankton is washed over the dam and fits the net size of one species or another of the net-spinners. That species explodes in numbers. That's why spotted sedges are so important on tailwaters.

Spotted sedge pupae emerge from the larval retreat, drift along the bottom for some distance, then are propelled to the surface by a combination of a swimming motion and a bubble of gas captured beneath the pupal skin. They come up fairly swiftly. The adult pops out as soon as the insect reaches the surface. It is able to escape into the air at once. You'll see splashy rises when this is going on, usually just at dusk, but trout will refuse your dry. It's usually because they're taking swimming pupae so near the surface that they cause a splash to erupt at the take.

The adults are gone quickly from the surface. They live from one to three weeks, mating on streamside foliage. Females then return to the water and dive into it, swimming to the bottom to lay their eggs on stones and bottom debris. It's important to recall this behavior when you're choosing a dressing to fish for the adult spotted sedge.

About twenty-five species of this group populate the West. Most streams have more than one of them. Spotted sedge hatches begin in June on most waters. July and August see the peak of most spotted sedge hatches but some continue on into September. I've been on the Bighorn River in Montana in September when they were so numerous you were in danger of inhaling them.

Daily emergence can be sprinkled throughout the afternoon, keeping trout interested for hours. It can also be condensed into the hour or so before dusk, and probably goes on after dark on many or even most days. When the hatch happens at dusk you'll see a frenzy of trout activity. It will be difficult to solve. I recommend that you recall the old wet fly when this happens. Trout are likely to be feeding on a combination of emerging pupae and diving adults. Your dry can go ignored among cavorting trout.

▮ Recognition

Spotted sedge larvae, like the green rock worms that give rise to gray sedges, are wormlike, fleshy, and rather plump for their length. They have anal hooks, and tufts of gills along the abdominal segments. They also have three hardened plates behind the head, unlike green rock worms, which have just one.

The pupae of all caddis are indeterminate, with the key features of the larvae abandoned and the key features of the adult concealed under the pupal skin. They are identified even by experts most often by association: pupae are captured, some preserved in alcohol, some allowed to transform to adults which are keyed out and the association made.

Adult spotted sedges are recognized by their size and coloration. You'll have to watch carefully to note their behavior of diving into the water to swim down and lay their eggs on the bottom.

SPOTTED SEDGE LARVA

■ Key Characteristics

Larvae: Pair of anal hooks.
Gill tufts at base of anal hooks.
Gill tufts on abdominal segments.
Three hardened plates behind head.
Size 10 to 16.
Color: Tan to bright green.
Pupae: Size 10 to 16.
Color: Tan to green.
Adults: Wings tan to brown, spotted.
Body tan to dark olive.
Antennae body
length.
Size 12 to 16.

SPOTTED SEDGE PUPA

SPOTTED SEDGE ADULT

JIM SCHOLLMEYER

■ Imitation

Be sure to carry imitations for each of the stages of this important insect. The Tan Caddis Larva fishes for many species. The Green Caddis Larva listed in the last chapter fishes for many others of this group. The March Brown Spider soft-hackled wet will work for both emerging pupae and diving adults. You might also want to try a standard winged Hare's Ear wet fly in the appropriate size for the diving adult.

TAN CADDIS LARVA

Tan Caddis Larva

Hook: Scud or bait hook, size 10 to 16.
Weight: 10 to 20 turns lead wire diameter of hook shank.
Thread: Brown 6/0 or 8/0 nylon.
Body: Tan fur or synthetic dubbing.
Legs: Brown partridge fibers.
Thorax: Brown fur or synthetic dubbing, picked out.

March Brown Spider (Sylvester Nemes)

Hook: 2X heavy, size 10 to 16.
Thread: Hot orange 6/0 nylon.
Hackle: Brown partridge, sparse.
Rib: Oval gold tinsel.
Body: Hare's mask fur.

MARCH BROWN SPIDER

Brown and Yellow Deep Sparkle Pupa

(Gary LaFontaine)
Hook: Standard dry fly, size 12 to 16.
Weight: 10 to 15 turns lead wire diameter of hook shank or one size finer.
Thread: Brown 6/0 or 8/0 nylon.
Overbody: Russet or gold Sparkle Yarn.

BROWN AND YELLOW DEEP SPARKLE PUPA

Underbody: 1/2 russet or gold Sparkle Yarn, 1/2 brown fur mixed and dubbed.
Legs and antennae: Wood duck flank fibers.
Head: Brown fur or synthetic.

Elk Hair Caddis
(Al Troth)

Hook: Standard dry fly, size 12 to 16.
Thread: Tan 6/0 or 8/0 nylon.
Rib: Fine gold wire, counterwound over hackle.
Hackle: Ginger, palmered over body.
Body: Tan fur or synthetic.
Wing: Natural elk hair or bleached coastal deer hair.

ELK HAIR CADDIS

Head: Clipped butts of wing fibers.
Note: In the smallest sizes, 16 and under, many guides and professional tiers prefer this fly without hackle. That is especially effective when it is to be fished on the smooth water where spotted sedges often hatch.

Tan X-Caddis
(John Juracek and Craig Mathews)

Hook: Standard dry fly, size 12 to 16.
Thread: Tan 6/0 or 8/0 nylon.
Tail: Amber Z-lon.
Body: Tan fur or synthetic.
Wing: Natural elk or bleached coastal deer hair.

TAN X-CADDIS

HARE'S EAR, WET

Hare's Ear, Wet
Hook: 2X stout, size 12 to 16.
Thread: Orange Gossamer silk or 6/0 nylon.
Tails: Pheasant tail fibers.
Rib: Small oval gold tinsel.
Body: Hare's mask fur, picked out at thorax for legs.
Wing: Hen pheasant secondary quill sections.

■ Presentation

Rig to fish the larval pattern with split shot and a strike indicator. The indicator should be fixed two to three times the depth of the water up the leader to start. If you're fishing slow water, move it down the leader; if the water is fast slide the indicator up the leader. Use enough shot to be sure you're hitting bottom now and then. These larvae do not swim. Tumble your imitation along every bit of the bottom in the riffle or run you're exploring.

Rig to fish pupal and adult patterns with the same terminal gear. Use a 10- to 12-foot leader tapered to 4X or 5X. Cast the pupa across-stream, be sure to get it under the surface, then let it swing down and around as slowly as possible. Mend the line and even toss slack into the drift to slow the fly. Be sure to fish the current seam between fast water and slow. The most likely moment for a strike during the swing is when the fly swims from a fast riffle or run into the slower water at its edge. That's where trout hold most often.

Most of the time, when fishing dry flies during this hatch, you'll be on the kind of rough water where an upstream presentation is not a problem. If you're fishing smooth flows, however, refine your gear down to 6X if necessary, and move into position to use the reach cast or downstream wiggle cast, in order to present the fly without frightening the fish with your line and leader.

CHAPTER 16

TERRESTRIAL BEETLES

Order: Coleoptera

BEETLES ARE OF SPORADIC IMPORTANCE IN THE WEST, but you cannot imagine a creek, stream, or river that does not have populations of them along it. There are 30,000 Western species. They have a place in every habitat niche, including aquatic forms that I'll ignore because they're so rarely concentrated that trout seldom feed selectively on them. It's terrestrial beetles that concern us here.

Terrestrial beetles are most important in forested environments, where populations are high and the wind often wafts them onto nearby lakes, ponds, and streams. They are also important in grassland and shrub environments, where they crawl along until they overhang water and drop in. Since that encompasses nearly all water types, you might find them important at times wherever you fish.

Beetles cause selective feeding most often where the water is smooth, and where good terrestrial habitat is set next to good habitat for trout. In other words, you'll fish beetles over selective trout only where you find good bank water that is somewhat smooth. That usually means an undercut, a back-eddy, or the outside sweep of a bend pool in a freestone stream, and anywhere the water is fairly deep along the edges of a spring creek or tailwater.

Beetles have complete metamorphosis. The larvae and pupae of terrestrial forms are not available to trout. Only the active adults get into trouble with trout.

Beetles, like all insects, are coldblooded. They are most abundant and active in late spring and summer, when the weather is warm: June, July, and August. They are not factors in winter, early spring, or in fall after the first freezing days. They are most active in the warm part of the day, late morning and through the afternoon, least active in the cool parts of the day, early morning and late evening. On days that are warm enough they'll be out and falling to the water in early evening as well.

■ Recognition

Beetles have hardened forewings held in carapace-fashion over their bodies. The aspect they present is of one large body segment behind the head. They are usually either round and portly—the lady-bug shape—or elongated and slender—the click beetle shape.

BEETLE

■ Key Characteristics

Shape, round or elongated.
Forewings as carapace over body.
Size 12 through 22.
Color: Various, commonly black or reddish.

■ Imitation

Natural beetles float awash in the surface film, half in and half out of it. They often struggle, and the only sign you see of them is a tiny set of concentric rings with a dot at the center. I believe that trout often key on the light pattern of those rings. Short of an undersized wind-up bathtub toy, I can't offer a solution to that. You do want to tie flies that lie with their bodies suspended in the film.

Tie your beetles on standard shank hooks to represent beetles with round bodies. Use 2X long hooks for those with long, slender bodies.

Black Crowe Beetle (John Crowe)
Hook: Standard dry fly or 2X long, size 12 to 22.
Thread: Black 6/0 or 8/0 nylon.
Body: Black deer hair overwound with black thread.
Legs: 3 body hair butts extended to each side, clipped short.
Shellback: Black-dyed deer hair, drawn over back.
Head: Butts of shellback hairs.

Note: The entire fly is tied with a single clump of dyed deer hair. Tie it on at the bend of the hook, with the tips extending to the back. Wrap it down to the mid-point of the hook, draw three fiber butts out to each side, and clip the rest. Gather the hair and twist it slightly, then draw it forward and tie it behind the hook eye. Whip-finish under the hair tips, at the eye. Clip them straight across to form the head.

BLACK CROWE BEETLE

FEATHERWING BEETLE

Featherwing Beetle

Hook: Standard dry fly or 2X long, size 12 to 22.
Thread: Black 6/0 or 8/0 nylon.
Body: Working thread.
Hackle: Black, palmered over body, clipped top and bottom.
Wing: Black hackle with fibers drawn back along stem.
Note: By drawing the fibers back tighter to the stem or more loosely, you can create a body that is slender or rounded. If you use a brown hackle and brown feather for the wing, you'll imitate reddish beetles.

Foam Beetle (Skip Morris)

Hook: Standard dry fly, size 8 to 18.
Thread: Black 6/0 or 8/0 nylon.
Legs: Black elk hair or fine rubber legs.
Body: Black foam.
Indicator: Yellow yarn.
Head: Butt of body foam.

FOAM BEETLE

▉ Presentation

Rig for the most refined presentations. Use light tackle, 2- through 4-weight rods, with floating lines. The leader should be 10 to 14 feet long, tapered to 5X or 6X, even 7X when fishing the tiniest flies on the smoothest water. It's more important to use three feet of any sized tippet than it is to fine it down to 7X, which will probably cost you many of the larger fish that you hook.

Look closely for sipping trout, which will almost always be tucked right against the edges of the stream, or along the shoreline of a lake or pond. Work as close as you can without alarming the trout, for a short and delicate cast. You'll need to be close in order to see the fly and follow its drift. Use whatever cast you can to get the fly in front of the trout without drag and without disturbing the fish with the passage of the line and leader. The reach cast and wiggle cast will almost always serve you better than an upstream cast that crosses the trout with the line and leader in the air.

Beetle imitations are difficult to follow on the water. When you see a sip in the area where your fly is floating, lift your rod gently to set the hook. If you set the hook hard you'll break off many of the large trout that sip selectively on tiny beetles.

CHAPTER 17

GRASSHOPPERS

Order: Orthoptera.

GRASSHOPPERS ARE LIKELY THE MOST IMPORTANT terrestrials to Western trout fishermen. They grow to large size, and interest the largest fish. They get onto the water in such numbers that trout position themselves for their arrival and await it expectantly, hanging along the streambanks and looking upward. At times so many land on the water that trout become selective to them, but that is not often the case. When it is, however, you're in for some of the most explosive fishing of the season.

Grasshoppers have weak flight muscles, strong legs to propel them into the air, and blocky, heavy bodies to weigh them down once they achieve flight. Their aerial maneuvers almost always consist of a long jump upward, then a descending slant to a controlled crash landing somewhere on the ground, or on water if that happens to be where they are headed. Wind sails them out over water and onto it often. With our vast Western sage and grasslands and pushy winds, it's easy to understand why grasshoppers cause excitement more often than terrestrials that crawl toward their engagements with trout.

As with all terrestrials, when hoppers land on water it tends to be along the edges. On a wide river, say the Deschutes or Madison, grasshopper activity is confined to ten to twenty feet alongside each bank. A mathematician could probably plot a "curve of most importance" for you that would show the number of hoppers landing on water diminishing exponentially with every yard you move away from the grasses at the very edge. You can plot your chances accordingly. Confine most of your hopper fishing to a yard or two out.

Grasshoppers are distributed in fishable numbers wherever grass and shrublands border streams. If you subtract the rainforest belt along the Northwest coast and the highest forested alpine creeks, that leaves the rest of the West. They're important in all major river valley systems, in every state and province. They're important in the semi-arid foothills on both sides of the Sierra, on the east side of the Cascades, and again on both sides of the Rockies, from south to north. They're important in some alpine meadow streams, and even in open forest where grass grows beneath tall trees.

Hoppers leave the egg when the ground begins to dry in spring. For the first month or two of their lives, they are nymphs, which essentially means grasshoppers without sufficient wing development to allow flight. That keeps them out of most trouble with trout.

Grasshoppers become mature, and most active, in the heat of summer. If the weather stays hot they'll keep flinging themselves into the air late into autumn. Their motors slow with the cold days of fall, and their importance to the angler ends at the same time.

Hoppers are most important in the middle of summer: July, August, and early September. If the weather remains hot they'll be important into early October in some stream systems.

Daily importance is during the hottest part of the day, from mid-morning through late afternoon and even into early evening. They are not active and do not often draw the notice of trout early and late in the day. Anything that serves to propel more hoppers into the air will be a stimulus to their daily importance. The passing of a harvesting machine through a streamside field of wheat will cause a feast for trout. A sudden rise of wind will propel hoppers over water. A cold cloud cover or sudden thunder shower will quell most hopper activity and diminish their importance.

GRASSHOPPER

■ Recognition

Hoppers have a shape so distinct it needs little description. Their bodies are blocky, their heads square. They have massive hind legs that are cocked under them like levered springs when the insect is at rest. If you need further confirmation, capture a specimen and see if it spits tobacco juice into your hand. Size is 6 down to 12, or even 14. Color is commonly a shade of pale to bright yellow, but olive hoppers figure into the mix. It's always best to get a good look at the color predominant on the stream you're about to fish.

■ Imitation

In the past I did most of my grasshopper fishing with a size 10 or 12 Elk Hair Caddis or Stimulator. I still use those dressings often when scattered hoppers are falling, when caddis are out exploring, and when trout are likely to be seeing a variety of things and not likely to be selective to any one of them. When hoppers are the obvious fare for the day, however, I now carry and fish specific grasshopper dressings. The main reason is the difference in the way hoppers ride the water. They are so heavy that they make a large dent in the surface film. Your fly should do the same: the bulk of the body should nearly outweigh whatever you have on the fly for flotation.

LETORT HOPPER

Letort Hopper (Ed Shenk)
Hook: 2X long, size 8 to 14.
Thread: Yellow 6/0 nylon.
Body: Yellow, olive, or mixed fur or synthetic.
Underwing: Mottled turkey tail feather section, sprayed with artist's fixative.
Overwing: Natural tan deer hair, spun as collar.
Head: Butts of deer hair wing, spun and clipped.

DAVE'S HOPPER

Dave's Hopper (Dave Whitlock)
Hook: 2X or 3X long, size 4 to 14.
Thread: Yellow 6/0 nylon.

Tail: Red deer hair over yellow Polypro yarn.
Rib: Brown hackle, trimmed.
Body: Yellow Polypro yarn.
Underwing: Pale yellow deer hair.
Overwing: Brown mottled turkey quill.
Legs: Yellow grizzly hackle stems, clipped and knotted.
Head: Deer hair, spun and clipped.
Collar: Tips of head hair.

HENRY'S FORK HOPPER

Henry's Fork Hopper (Mike Lawson)
Hook: 2X long, size 6 to 14.
Thread: Yellow 3/0 Monocord.
Body: Cream elk hair, tied reversed and extended.
Underwing: Yellow elk hair.
Overwing: Mottled brown hen saddle feather, sprayed with artist's fixative.
Head: Gray elk hair, bullet style.
Legs: Light yellow rubber legs.

■ Presentation

Rig for hopper fishing according to the conditions in which you'll fish them. If the water is smooth and the day windless, you might want a leader 12 feet or longer tapered to 5X. If you're bank fishing, the wind is blowing, and you're casting large patterns to tight pockets, rig with a leader about the length of your rod, tapered to 3X or 4X.

Always cast the fly to the water as gently as you can, and achieve as near to a perfect drag-free float as possible. If that fails to raise any trout, however, try splatting the fly to the water, let it drift a short way, then give it some twitches. Hoppers are never glad to land on water. They land with smacks, then struggle with those powerful hind legs. The struggle doesn't accomplish much for the unhappy hopper, but the hard landing and subsequent kicking often draw the attention of trout. If that is what does it, then cast hard, twitch the fly, and be prepared to hang on when a trout hits. Don't go below 4X tippet when you fish hoppers with such indelicacy.

CHAPTER 18

TRICOS

Order: Ephemeroptera
Family: Leptohyphidae
Genus: *Tricorythodes*
Species: *minutus*

THE TRICO IS THE TINIEST WESTERN MAYFLY HATCH and yet one of the most important. Wherever conditions are correct for them, they come off in such great numbers that they cause even large trout to move into the best feeding lanes, to sip them at leisure and very selectively. They are most important in meadow streams, spring creeks, tailwaters, and the lower reaches of some of our largest trout rivers. They are least important in boisterous freestone streams.

Tricos are often important in Western trout Meccas: Silver Creek and the Henry's Fork in Idaho, the Bighorn in Montana, the San Juan in New Mexico, Hat Creek in California, the Bow in Alberta, too many other famous places to mention. But they also hatch in great numbers in streams and rivers with less recognition, all over the West. The lower ends of rivers, in their pastoral valley reaches that are not fished often, might have excellent Trico hatches, while the upper and sometimes more famous reaches might not.

Tricos have a one-year life cycle. Like all mayflies they have incomplete metamorphosis, going through nymph, dun, and spinner stages. The nymphs are taken by trout in great numbers, but I've never noticed that they're taken selectively, though of course it could happen. They have what entomologists call *operculate* gills: the front pair of gills form a lid over all the others. This protects them from silt. The gill lid is lifted briefly to allow water to percolate through the others, providing oxygen. Then the lid is lowered to prevent silt from clogging the working gills.

Trico nymphs are able to live in water that is too laden with fine particles and silt for most mayfly species. Their populations are excellent in slow spring creeks and tailwaters, but also in the lower regions of rivers where most insect hatches have petered out. They are rarely found in fishable numbers in tumbling headwaters or in the fast currents of typical freestone stretches of streams.

When mature, Trico emergence can take place in one of the three ways typical of other mayflies. The nymph can split the skin on the stream bottom, and the dun emerges there to make its way to the top. The nymph might swim to the top where emergence takes place in the surface film. Or the nymph might migrate to shore and crawl out on a rock or vegetation for emergence. No matter how emergence is accomplished, the dun makes its way into the air with some haste, and in scattered numbers. Trout feed on them when they can, but the dun is not the most important stage of the insect.

Molting from the dun to spinner stage takes place alongside the stream or in the air, within a few minutes to a day after emergence. Mating is done in the air, at times a half hour after emergence and the quick molt to the spinner stage. In its briefest form, the adult life lasts less than an hour, from emergence to molt to mating to laying the eggs and falling spent to the water. More often, the dun flies to streamside vegetation, molts to the spinner stage, remains hidden and cryptic overnight, then returns to mate over the stream in the first warmth of the next morning, lay eggs, and fall spent. These massed morning spinner falls are the most important time in the cycle.

Seasonal importance begins in late June on some lowland streams, continues through early October, though not necessarily as you move eastward and upward. The peak of the hatch in the Rockies and almost everywhere else is in August and September. It can go on for several weeks on the same stream.

Daily spinner falls begin as early as 7:00 a.m., but more often start between 9:00 and 11:00. If the angle of the sun is right, you'll see the glints of their wings in the air, sometimes so dense they form a mist rising above the true morning mist off the river. At other times they're almost impossible to see. The first thing you notice are trout rising with delicate sips in the very smoothest of currents, with nothing apparent on the water to cause this feeding. If you don't get your nose to the surface quickly for a close examination, you might miss the entire show. Sometimes it lasts only an hour, rarely much more than two. You should be prepared for the Trico spinner fall in order to avoid the frustration of fishing through it without even knowing you're doing it.

■ Recognition

Tricos are tiny. They arise from crawler nymphs, so they have three tails in both the dun and important spinner stages. Their key characteristics are their tiny size, three tails, and the absence of hindwings.

■ Key Characteristics

Spinners: Three tails.
Hindwings absent.
Forewings usually spent on the water.
Color: Body green in females, dark brown to black in males.
Size 20 to 26.

TRICO SPINNER

■ Imitation

I've had excellent luck on Trico No-Hackle dressings, though I don't use them often due to the fragility of their wings. I think they work well because the wings stand up and are relatively easy to see, for a fly tied on size 20 and smaller hooks. I also believe that size and to a certain extent shape, are most important during a hatch of such tiny insects. Be sure to use your aquarium net to capture a few specimens. Compare the size of your fly directly to a natural upon which the trout are known to be feeding.

Most of the flies tied to represent Tricos should be tied spent, as spinners, and in either olive for the females or black for the males.

TRICO NO-HACKLE

Trico No-Hackle (Doug Swisher and Carl Richards)
Hook: Standard dry fly, size 20 to 26.

Thread: Black 8/0 nylon.
Tails: White Micro Fibetts, split.
Body: Black fur or synthetic.
Wings: White or light gray mallard or teal wing
   segments.
Head: Black fur or synthetic.

OLIVE POLYWING TRICO

Olive Polywing Trico
Hook: Standard dry fly, size 20 to 26.
Thread: Olive 8/0 nylon.
Tails: White Micro Fibetts, split.
Abdomen: Olive fur or synthetic dubbing.
Wing: White or light gray Polypro yarn, spent.
Thorax: Dark brown fur or synthetic dubbing.

BLACK POLYWING TRICO

Black Polywing Trico
Hook: Standard dry fly, size 20 to 26.
Thread: Black 8/0 nylon.
Tails: White Micro Fibetts, split.
Abdomen: Dark brown fur or synthetic dubbing.
Wings: White or light gray Polypro yarn, spent.
Thorax: Black fur
   or synthetic
   dubbing.

Trico Quill Spinner
(A.K. Best)
Hook: Standard
   dry fly, size 20
   to 26.
Thread: Black 8/0
   nylon.

TRICO QUILL SPINNER

Tails: White hackle fibers, split, 1-1/2 times length of hook.
Abdomen: Pale-green-dyed hackle stem.
Wing: White hen hackle tips.
Thorax: Black fur or synthetic dubbing.
Hackle: Black, trimmed on top and bottom.

CDC TRICO SPINNER

CDC Trico Spinner
Hook: Standard dry fly, size 20 to 26.
Thread: Black 8/0 nylon.
Wings: White CDC fibers.
Tails: White hackle fibers, split.
Body: Olive or black fur or synthetic dubbing.

■ Presentation

Rig for fishing these tiniest of flies with the finest of gear. Your rod is especially important. Its tip must be soft enough to protect 6X tippets on the hook set. Most 2- to 4-weight rods will do it, but you'll find some that are so stiff you'll constantly break off and wonder why. The leader should be twelve to fourteen feet long, with around three feet of 6X tippet.

Your position should be close enough to rising trout to hit them on the nose. They'll be concentrating on a feeding lane, and will not move more than a few inches out of it to take a tiny fly, especially when lots of naturals are adrift. Whether you cast upstream, across with a reach cast, or downstream with a wiggle cast, be sure that the trout sees the fly and only a few inches of leader. Be sure you are getting a drag-free float. Be delicate enough that you can make the same presentation repeatedly to the same trout without putting it down.

Even if everything is perfect on the first and many subsequent casts, the trout might refuse for no fault of yours. Persistence, delicacy, and accuracy are the names of the Trico game.

CHAPTER 19

FALL CADDIS

Order: Trichoptera
Family: Limnephilidae
Genus: *Dicosmoecus* (three Western species);
       Onocosmoecus (two Western species)

THE FALL CADDIS ARE A PROMINANT WESTERN GROUP of insects, but I'm not sure how important they are. They are big and abundant on my home river, the Deschutes. They bound around at streamside in the late afternoon and evening. Females lay their eggs out over the water. I have seen them dipping down time after time to touch their abdomen to a prime run of edge water that I know holds trout. I always expect to see the kind of detonation I know a salmonfly would cause in the same situation. But it doesn't happen, and I don't know why.

I catch fish on fall caddis imitations at times, but no more consistently than I would on an Elk Hair Caddis or Stimulator fished at the same time. I believe I'm overlooking fall caddis pupae, which are large, corpulent, and available along the edges. But I'm telling you all this because fall caddis are so big and so common that they cannot be ignored, yet it's easy to give them more importance than I've found that they warrant in my own fishing.

One species or another of the fall caddis group lives in nearly every trout stream from California to British Columbia, from New Mexico through Montana to Alberta. They are abundant in coastal rivers, present in Sierra and Cascade streams, and are scattered throughout the Rockies. They live in small streams and large rivers, though not often in the downstream end of systems where clean stones give way to silt bottoms. They are not particularly important in spring creeks and tailwaters, being more abundant on freestone streams with frequent riffles and vigorous runs.

On my small streams in the coastal hills of Oregon, they are a great presence before a watershed is logged. You cannot wade without crunching an occasional larval case. After logging, when silt settles in, their populations are reduced to perhaps a tenth of what they were when the stones were clean.

Fall caddis have a one- to three-year life cycle. The larvae build cases of gravel and sand, the weight of the case depending on the speed of the water in which they live. The faster the water, the heavier the case, which acts as ballast to keep them on the bottom. The larvae are large in the latest instars, and are taken by trout case and all. The occasional trout you catch with gravel in its stomach has not been eating stones off the bottom; it has eaten a fall caddis larva or two, and digested all the fleshy parts. But I don't consider the larvae important for imitation.

Before pupation, the larvae migrate toward quiet water at the shore or near it, and often gather in colonies. The larval case is sealed to a rock, and pupation takes place inside. It takes several weeks. When complete, the pupa cuts its way out of the stone case, crawls and swims the rest of the way to shore along the bottom, then either swims up or climbs up on emergent rocks. I suspect this takes place at evening or after dark, but have no proof of it. I often see cast skins on rocks right at the waterline. I believe a pupal dressing might be the answer more often than I attempt to use it.

The adults hang out in streamside grasses and vegetation for several weeks. You can see them on frosty fall mornings, cryptic and hiding. If you touch one it lets go its grip and simply falls into deeper hiding, no doubt a defense against birds that nose along and pick them like fat berries.

Mating takes place on vegetation. Female fall caddis return to the water to lay their eggs, or sow the eggs to the undersides of leaves overhanging the water. This is a defense against trout predation, and might be a major reason some fall caddis are not as important as their size and numbers indicate they should be. But others lay their eggs by touching their abdomen to the water to wash the eggs off the end. These are taken often enough that a dressing for them works when you see adults bouncing around.

Fall caddis, it should not surprise you, are important in September, October, and on into November. Because the adults live several weeks, numbers of them are out daily during much of that time.

Daily importance begins in early to late afternoon, when the adults get active and begin making sorties from shore out over the edges of the stream or river. Activity goes on into evening, especially on warm fall days.

■ Recognition

The key characteristics to recognition of these insects are the time of abundance and the size of the individuals. They are out in fall; they are the largest caddis you will see in that season.

■ Key Characteristics

Adult: Heavily veined or mottled gray to brown wings. Long antennae. Size 6 to 10.
Color: Yellow to orange body.

FALL CADDIS

■ Imitation

I believe the pupa is overlooked and the adult overrated. Carry dressings for both, but try the wet patterns as often as you try the dry. The results might surprise you. If you fish in waters such as the Deschutes, with populations of trout and fall migrations of steelhead, the results of fishing a large caddis pupal pattern on the swing might be quite a commotion.

DARK CADDIS EMERGENT

Dark Caddis Emergent (Polly Rosborough)
Hook: 1X long, size 6 to 10.
Thread: Black 3/0 Monocord.
Body: Burnt orange fur or synthetic, as noodle.
Hackle: Dark furnace, clipped top and bottom.
Head: Black ostrich herl.

Brown and Orange Deep Sparkle Pupa (Gary LaFontaine)
Hook: Standard dry fly, size 6 to 10.
Weight: 15 to 20 turns lead wire, or underweight.
Thread: Brown 6/0 or 8/0 nylon.
Overbody: Orange Sparkle Yarn.
Underbody: 1/2 rusty-orange fur, 1/2 orange Sparkle Yarn, mixed and dubbed.

Hackle: Dark grouse fibers.
Head: Cinnamon marabou or fur.

Orange Bucktail Caddis

Hook: Standard dry fly, size 8 to 12.
Thread: Black 6/0 nylon.
Hackle: Brown, palmered over body.
Body: Orange fur or synthetic dubbing.
Wing: Natural brown deer body hair.

ORANGE BUCKTAIL CADDIS

Fall Caddis

Hook: 2X long, size 6 to 12.
Thread: Black 6/0 nylon.
Body hackle: Brown, undersized.
Body: Orange fur or synthetic.
Wing: Natural brown deer body hair.
Hackle: Brown saddle.

FALL CADDIS

■ Presentation

Carry a somewhat stout outfit to propel these large flies if they're all you'll be fishing on a given day, which in reality is not likely. A 5- or 6-weight floating line is about right. I usually fish fall caddis patterns for trout in the afternoon on the same days that I fish the Deschutes at dawn and dusk for summer steelhead, so I use the same outfit: a 6-weight rod armed with a weight-forward, 7-weight floater. It's just right for large fall caddis flies, though a bit stiff for presentation fishing. The leader should be eight to ten feet long; you'll be fishing the edges and will need control of the cast to pinpoint it into holding lies. Taper it to 3X or at most 4X.

If you tie a pupal pattern to the tippet, fish it down and around on a slow swing that brings it swimming right to the bank. That's where most takes will happen.

If you fish dries, wade at the edges or stay out of the water. Tuck your casts right up against the banks, especially in places where alders or other trees sweep out over the water. It sometimes works well to dap these flies downstream along the banks, giving them an occasional twitch as they drift back beneath overhanging leaves and limbs.

Try all sorts of presentations with fall caddis dressings. In truth I've not worked out the answers to my own satisfaction.

CHAPTER 20

SCUDS

Order: Crustacea
Genera: *Gammarus, Hyallela*

SCUDS ARE STILL- AND SLOW-WATER DWELLERS THAT are important in nearly all Western lakes and ponds, and also in many streams and rivers that are idle enough for weed growth to take root. That usually means a tailwater or spring creek.

They are most abundant in lakes and ponds with lots of vegetation, least abundant where the water is more sterile. They are important in alkaline desert lakes with good weed growth, less important in alpine lakes where the water is clear and growth sparse. However, they do grow to good size in some alpine lakes, and should never be overlooked there if you can peer into the water and spot weed beds. Scuds will gather, and so will trout.

Scuds are distributed all through the West in waters where conditions are right for them. They are most important in high desert environments because the alkaline soil favors the growth of the chitinous crustacean. They are more abundant in limestone spring creeks in the East and Midwest, while favoring tailwaters in the arid country of the West because our spring creeks normally arise from volcanic sources, and are comparatively sterile in terms of suspended calcium compounds.

A tailwater like the Lees Ferry stretch of the Colorado, impounded over desert soils rich in calcareous compounds, is rich in scuds. A tailwater like the Deschutes, arising from a lava aquifer poor in calcium, has less-important populations of scuds. Almost all lakes have scuds, most of them in important populations.

Scuds have no aerial stage, so you cannot mark their presence by a flight of adult scuds in the air. It's always wise to run a collecting net through weed beds in any new river or lake that you fish. If scuds are present and dominant, they'll announce themselves in the meshes, and you should try their imitations.

Scuds are in the water all year around, swimming, breeding, eating and being eaten. They do not emerge as adults and disappear during the egg stage and early instars as aquatic insects do. If the population is good, they are simply present and available for trout whenever something else is not more abundant and more easily accessed because of its life cycle. That makes scuds important whenever other food forms are not.

Seasonally, scuds pick up the slack in the trout diet during those times when aquatic insects are in the egg stage or the earliest, tiniest instars. That makes scuds important in early spring if the water is ice-free, in late summer and fall if aquatic insect hatches have emerged, and in winter if the water is open to fishing. Scuds are important all season if they are the dominant food form even when something else is active or hatching. In that case, fish with flies that imitate them at any time of year. But most often, scuds enjoy their moment of most importance in fall and winter fisheries.

Their daily cycle is tied somewhat to water temperature. They'll be most active when the water is warmest during the cold season, which is when you're most likely to be fishing their imitations. That's the time of day trout are most active, as well. Usually that means the hours in the middle of the day, from about 10:00 a.m. until 3:00 or 4:00 p.m. In winter fishing, that about makes a day of fishing me.

■ Recognition

Scuds are crustaceans. Their exoskeleton is continuous, a hardened and shiny segmented shellback from stem to stern. They have paired swimmer legs on the abdominal segments, which are a-whirr when the insect is in water. They take a curved shape when removed from water, but this is deceiving; they are straight and sticklike when swimming in natural conditions, which is the way trout see them. Scuds also change color when removed from water. Be sure to observe them as soon as you collect them, to get the color of your imitation correct. If you pickle them in alcohol and tie flies to imitate them when you get

SCUD

home, you'll have creations trout have never seen. Of course, that does not mean they will not catch fish.

■ Key Characteristics

Continuous segmented shellback.
Swimmer legs on abdominal segments.
Curved shape when removed from water.
Size from 10 to too small to imitate.
Color: Usually a shade of olive, tan, or gray.

■ Imitation

Be sure that your imitation captures the sticklike swimming posture of the natural, not the curved shape of a scud out of water. Also be sure to capture the color the trout see, not what you see after you preserve a scud in alcohol. I believe the key to a good imitation is the working of the fur on the underside, which looks like the continual movement of all those swimmer legs on the natural.

OLIVE SCUD

Olive Scud

Hook: 2X heavy, size 12 to 20.
Weight: 10 to 15 turns lead wire.
Thread: Olive 6/0 or 8/0 nylon.
Tails: Olive-dyed partridge fibers.
Shellback: Ziploc baggie material, ribbed with
    thread.
Body: Olive fur or synthetic dubbing, picked out.
Antennae: Olive-dyed partridge fibers.

GRAY SCUD

Gray Scud

Hook: 2X heavy, size 12 to 20.

Weight: 10 to 15 turns lead wire.
Thread: Gray 6/0 or 8/0 nylon.
Tails: Gray partridge fibers.
Shellback: Ziploc baggie material, ribbed with thread.
Body: Gray fur or synthetic dubbing, picked out.
Antennae: Gray partridge fibers.

TAN SCUD

Tan Scud
Hook: 2X heavy, size 12 to 20.
Weight: 10 to 15 turns lead wire.
Thread: Tan 6/0 or 8/0 nylon.
Tails: Brown partridge fibers.
Shellback: Ziploc baggie material, ribbed with thread.
Body: Tan fur or synthetic dubbing, picked out.
Antennae: Brown partridge fibers.

LEES FERRY SHRIMP

Lees Ferry Shrimp (Len Holt)
Hook: 2X long, size 10 to 14.
Thread: Tan 3/0 Monocord.
Tail and shellback: Bleached deer or elk hair, ribbed with working thread.
Body: Tan Antron yarn, picked out.

■ Presentation

When fishing scud imitations in moving water, rig with the strike indicator and split shot method. Fish the nymphs dead-drift and tumbling along the bottom. In the circle of friends with whom I fish, winter fishing is often done with a size 12 to 14 weighted scud dressing just below the shot, a smaller nymph on a 10- to 12-inch dropper tied to the bend of the scud dressing. Trout take one or the other about equally.

For lake fishing with scud dressings, choose the line sink rate that will reach the weed beds over which you are fishing. At times that will be a floating line with a long leader. Most often in my own fishing, it's a wet-tip line. At times it takes a fast or even extra-fast sinking line to get down to the depth you want.

Use the countdown method to explore stillwater depths. Start counting the fly down fifteen seconds, retrieving with a slow hand-twist. Add five seconds to the count on each subsequent cast until you retrieve weeds or hook a trout. Continue at that depth, or a bit shallower, and you'll be in the zone where natural scuds, and the trout that live upon them, hang around. Have patience; it often takes a lot of casts to connect in this sort of exploratory fishing.

For that reason, I often like to cast a scud dressing on a sinking line over the stern of my float tube or pram, and explore by paddling idly around a lake. I know it's not the most exciting form of fly fishing, but it lets me prowl to see what I can see and probe the depths at the same time. I'm happy with that. Troll slowly.

CHAPTER 21

LEECHES

Order: Hirudinea

LEECHES, LIKE SCUDS, HAVE A LEVEL OF IMPORTANCE that does not rise and fall abruptly based on some sort of migration or hatch. They are out there all the time, most often in lakes but also in some rivers, especially the silty, weedy lower reaches where large trout hang out. That makes leeches most important when some other food form, say a mayfly, caddis, or stonefly, is not migrating or emerging and thus commanding the attention of the trout. If a leech, or its imitation, swims by when a trout's focus is not elsewhere, the trout is almost always willing to whack it. For some reason, even where populations of leeches are low, trout have a special memory about the last time they had one, and they're eager to get the next one.

Leeches live in lakes and ponds in all regions of the West. They are most abundant where aquatic vegetation is heaviest. Their greatest populations might be in thin, weedy lake and pond shallows that are not suitable habitat for trout, except when they nose into them on hunting expeditions. I once wiggled a canoe paddle in inches of water in a backwater bay of a large lake in the Kamloops region of British Columbia. Big leeches galloped toward the disturbance from all directions. I withdrew the paddle in fright.

Leeches are important in stillwaters and some streams in the mountains of New Mexico north to the Bighorn in Montana and the Bow in Alberta. They reach their peak of importance in the Kamloops region of B.C., and are abundant all the way south to California. They are more important in stillwaters than they are in rivers. Weed beds in six to ten feet of water are their prime habitat, though they are also abundant down on the bottom in the marl depths of many lakes and ponds.

Leeches are omnivorous, eating vegetable matter and any insects and decaying animal matter they come across. The myriad of planktonic forms that live pelagically—not in association with the shoreline—and that die out in open water and settle to the bottom to form that soft marl layer, make perfect habitat for bottom-dwelling leeches. In shallower water they prowl the bottom or among the weeds, hunting for whatever they can find to eat.

Their movements are slow, not unlike that of earthworms, when they are not disturbed or after prey. When in a hurry they swim with an undulating movement similar to that of a snake, though their progress is not exactly swift. It's likely that a leech can sense the presence of a trout on its tail, and that it turns on its afterburners when pursued.

Leeches are not on a boom and bust one-year life cycle. They're out there available to trout all year long. Their feeding movements keep them distributed widely, so that you rarely run into trout feeding selectively on them.

Being present at all seasons, leeches become most important when trout are not focused on something else. That can mean the heat of summer, when stillwaters stratify and the trout sink into the depths and the doldrums. A leech makes an excellent searching pattern for trout that are down and not moving much. In fall, when lakes turn over and most aquatic insect activity is at an end, leeches continue to be excellent dressings to interest trout eager to stoke up fuel for the winter ahead. If the water is open to winter fishing, leech dressings increase in importance as other things become less active, and their imitations less useful. I can't say if this is based on the continued activity of leeches in cold water, or more probably the long memory trout have about the last leech they've eaten.

Daily importance is not restricted to any particular time. Leeches are blind, and hunt at all hours. I would simply recommend fishing a leech dressing when you have no indication that something else would be better. An abundance of scuds or some aquatic insect might tip you toward using something other than a leech pattern. In the absence of such indications, leech dressings are hard to beat in any water where the naturals are present, whether it's a lake or a stream.

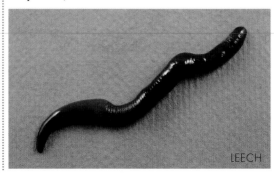

LEECH

■ Recognition

Leeches, when stretched to full length, resemble earth-worms that have been somewhat flattened, and that have sucking discs at each end. When recoiled they tuck into the rounded shape of a coin, or some posture between stretched out and rounded. When trout see them, it's probable that they're most often in the stretched position, swimming fast. They vary in length from five inches down to an inch or so.

■ Key Characteristics

Shape: Earthworm-like to rounded.
Suckers at each end.
Size 5" down to 1".
Color: Most are black, olive, or blood red, or
tan to olive with spots.

■ Imitation

It's critical to note that while leeches get very large, most trout seem to take smaller ones that are in the 1 1/2- to 2 1/2-inch range. I have not found the largest leeches in trout stomachs I've examined, and other writers report the same thing. It's quite common to find the remains of two or three leeches around two inches long in a trout that lives in excellent habitat where large leeches abound. Your leech imitations should be tied on size 6 to 12 hooks, not the largest sizes in which you might find a local leech.

BLACK WOOLLY BUGGER

Black Woolly Bugger
Hook: 3X long, size 6 to 12.
Weight: 15 to 20 turns lead wire, diameter of the hook shank.
Thread: Black 6/0 nylon.
Tail: Black marabou.
Hackle: Black, palmered over body.
Body: Black chenille.

OLIVE WOOLLY BUGGER

Olive Woolly Bugger
Hook: 3X long, size 6 to 12.
Weight: 15 to 20 turns lead wire.
Thread: Olive 6/0 nylon.
Tail: Olive marabou.
Hackle: Brown, palmered over body.
Body: Olive chenille.

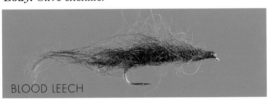

BLOOD LEECH

Blood Leech
Hook: 3X long, size 6 to 12.
Weight: 15 to 20 turns lead wire.
Thread: Brown 6/0 nylon.
Body and tail: Reddish brown Mohair yarn, teased out.

BLACK MARABOU LEECH

Black Marabou Leech
Hook: 3X long, size 6 to 12.
Weight: 15 to 20 turns lead wire.

Thread: Black 6/0 nylon.
Tail: Black marabou.
Body: Black chenille.
Wing: Black marabou.

OLIVE MARABOU LEECH

Olive Marabou Leech
Hook: 3X long, size 6 to 12.
Weight: 15 to 20 turns lead wire.
Thread: Olive 6/0 nylon.
Tail: Olive marabou.
Body: Olive chenille.
Wing: Olive marabou.

■ Presentation

There are at least three, and probably many more, ways to fish a leech dressing. The first is simply to cast it out and let it slip into darkness, without any retrieve at all. This requires a wet-head or full-sink line of a sink rate fast enough to get the fly to the bottom. Once it's there, hand-twist retrieve it back at an agonizingly slow pace. I've seen this method be very effective for folks with more patience then I happen to have.

The second way is to cast the leech dressing out in somewhat weedy water, let it sink at least part way to the weed tops, then begin a fast stripping retrieve. This imitates a leech away from protéctive cover, with its afterburners turned on as if a trout were in pursuit. When a trout happens onto the fleeing leech, the fish is not smart enough to realize that it did not trigger the flight. At least that's the way I've got it all figured out. This method works well for me at times, totally fails at others. When it works it draws tremendous strikes. I usually use a wet-tip line in extra fast sinking.

The third method for fishing the leech is to cast it over the stern of a float tube or boat and troll with it. Use a line that will get it down nearly to the bottom in the depth you're fishing. Move as slowly as you can. I often use a midge dressing, the TDC, as a dropper a couple of feet in front of the leech. It's easy to imagine that a trout thinks the tandem is a leech chasing a midge, but I doubt if trout consider it to that extent. They see one or the other or both, and take the one that appeals to them most for reasons that trout have and keep to themselves.

One last note on leeches. When a trout takes one, it opens its mouth, flares its gills, and inhales the luckless creature. If it's a natural leech, it backs right into the trout's mouth. If it's your fly, it's tethered to your leader and remains right where it is when the trout inhales, to the surprise of the trout. You'll feel a slight tap and instinctively set the hook. The trout will swing around to try to take the leech again and it will be gone, because you've set the hook and yanked it out of there. It's all a mystery to the fish.

To avoid this, when you feel the tap of a take, drop your rod tip. Wait a beat or two, then lift your rod. You'll be amazed how often the trout has made that swing, inhaled again, and you feel weight when you lift the rod. Your leech dressing, released from the tension of the line and leader, drifts right into the trout's mouth.

Now set the hook and hold on.

BIBLIOGRAPHY

Almy, Gerald: *Tying & Fishing Terrestrials.* Harrisburg: Stackpole Books, 1978.

Arbona, Fred L. Jr.: *Mayflies, the Angler, and the Trout.* Tulsa: Winchester Press, 1980.

Best, A. K.: *A. K.'s Fly Box.* New York: Lyons & Burford, 1996.

Brooks, Charles E.: *The Trout and the Stream.* New York: Crown, 1974.

Brooks, Charles E.: *Nymph Fishing for Larger Trout.* New York: Crown, 1976.

Hafele, Rick and Dave Hughes: *The Complete Book of Western Hatches.* Portland: Frank Amato Publications, Inc., 1981.

Hafele, Rick and Scott Roederer: *An Angler's Guide to Aquatic Insects and Their Imitations.* Boulder: Johnson Books, 1987.

Juracek, John and Craig Mathews: *Fishing Yellowstone Hatches.* West Yellowstone: Blue Ribbon Flies, 1992.

Kaufmann, Randall: *Fly Patterns of Umpqua Feather Merchants.* Glide: Umpqua Feather Merchants, 1995.

LaFontaine, Gary: *Caddisflies.* New York: Lyons & Burford, 1981.

Morris, Skip: *Tying Foam Flies.* Portland: Frank Amato Publications, Inc., 1994.

Nemes, Sylvester: *Soft-Hackled Fly Imitations.* Harrisburg: Stackpole Books, 1981.

Rosborough, E. H. "Polly": *Tying and Fishing the Fuzzy Nymphs.* Harrisburg: Stackpole Books, 1988.

Schollmeyer, Jim: *Hatch Guide For the Lower Deschutes River.* Portland: Frank Amato Publications, Inc., 1994.

Schollmeyer, Jim: *Hatch Guide For Lakes.* Portland: Frank Amato Publications, Inc., 1995.

Schollmeyer, Jim: *Hatch Guide For Western Streams.* Portland: Frank Amato Publications, Inc., 1997.

Schwiebert, Ernest: *Nymphs.* New York: Winchester Press, 1973.

Stetzer, Randle Scott: *Flies: The Best One Thousand.* Portland: Frank Amato Publications, Inc., 1992.

WESTERN HATCH CHART

Natural	Emergence Period		Daily Emergence	
	Coast	Rockies	Fall/Winter/Early Spring	Late Spring/Early Summer
Midges	Jan.-Dec.	Jan.-Dec.	11 a.m.-3 p.m.	All day
Little Olives	Feb.-Nov.	Apr.-Oct.	12 a.m.-4 p.m.	10 a.m.-4 p.m.
Western March Browns	Mar.-May	Apr.-Jun.	1 p.m.-3 p.m.	11 a.m.-3 p.m.
Speckle-wing Quills	Apr.-Oct.	May-Oct.	12 a.m.-3 p.m.	10 a.m.-4 p.m.
American Grannoms	Apr.-Oct.	May-Sep.	Spring 1 p.m.-3 p.m.	Fall 1 p.m.-dark
Salmonflies	May-Jun.	Jun.-Jul.	5 p.m.-dark	5 p.m.-dark
Golden Stones	May-Jun.	Jun.-Aug.	Dusk	Dusk
Western Green Drakes	Apr-Sep	May-Sep.	1 p.m.-3 p.m.	11 a.m.-3 p.m.
Green Damsels	May-Jul.	May-Jul.	Migrate afternoon and evenings	

Ants	Apr.-Oct.	May-Oct.	Warmest part of the day
Pale Morning Duns	May-Aug.	May-Aug.	11 a.m.-3 p.m. 9 a.m.-5 p.m.
Gray Drakes	May-Jun.	Jun.-Jul.	Afternoon and evening spinner falls
Gray Sedges	May-Sep.	Jun.-Sep.	1 p.m.-4 p.m. 11 a.m.-5 p.m.
Spotted Sedges	May-Sep.	Jun.-Sep.	1 p.m.-Dusk 1 p.m.-Dusk
Terrestrial Beetles	May-Oct.	May-Oct.	Active warm part of day
Grasshoppers	Jun.-Oct.	Jun.-Oct.	Active warm part of day
Tricos	Jul.-Oct.	Jul.-Oct.	11 a.m.-1 p.m. 9 a.m.-11 a.m.
Fall Caddis	Sep.-Oct.	Sep.-Oct.	Most active late afternoon and evening
Scuds	Present all year		Active all day
Leeches	Present all year		Active all day

Note: All emergence times are the most common for the given group.
Variations in species, latitude, and altitude cause common movements outside the averages.